max's
kansas city
STORIES

max's kansas city STORIES

Tony Weinberger

THE BOBBS–MERRILL COMPANY, INC.
Indianapolis • Kansas City • New York

THE BOBBS-MERRILL COMPANY, INC.
A Subsidiary of Howard W. Sams & Co., Inc., Publishers
Indianapolis/Kansas City/New York
Copyright © 1971 by Anthony D. Weinberger
All rights reserved
Library of Congress catalog card number: 77-142481
Manufactured in the United States
First printing

This book is for WILLIE SUTTON and DIANE WAKOSKI

—through metaphor to reconcile
the people and the stones.
Compose. (No ideas
but in things) Invent!
Saxifrage is my flower that splits
the rocks.

from "A Sort of a Song"
© 1944 William Carlos Williams

CONTENTS

max's kansas city

STORIES

THE SINK

SAM AND I were driving downtown on The Bowery. It was the last business day before Christmas, which that year fell on a Monday, and raining. We were looking for a secondhand kitchen sink and base cabinet. It had to have a sliding drainboard. I had told the architect for whom I was building the loft that the sink that I had bought for him had a sliding drainboard and so that was what it had to have. It also had to be a pressed-steel sink (we had already seen several heavy cast-iron ones), because it was to be installed in a top-floor loft in a building without an elevator. There had once been an elevator; in fact the shaftway still existed on that floor.

Emmett, an underground film maker who loved all orifices, had the two floors below. He was the titular super and for sweeping the halls once a month, if he was straight enough, he got one floor for half rent. The owner was a widowed lady living in Yonkers who had never seen

1

the building and thought this a fair exchange. Emmett
had originally had one floor and appropriated the roof
whenever he needed a location for an outdoor orgy scene,
which in his films was quite often. The roof was quite
sequestered as it was a seven-story building, and he had a
garden up there of hundreds of potted cacti, some of them
quite large. It was said by the artists in the neighborhood
that he grew his own peyote buttons up there.

Formerly he had been an electronic composer support-
ing himself as a pot connection. He had been struck by
the police one night when they came in through a trap-
door in the elevator tower on the roof. A friend with
good connections in the real world immediately got him
a prestigious grant for his music and this so impressed
the judge that he was put on probation. That way he
neither spent time in jail nor had to get a job. But he
had to stop selling pot. That's when he switched from
hemp plants to cacti on the roof.

Every spring the cacti in their hundreds of pots had to
be moved three flights up to the roof and every fall, down.
He had made his first movie that way. He had a large
party, figuring to divide the work. Someone brought a
super-8 movie camera. As the carriers got more and more
stoned, undirected couplings in every conceivable permu-
tation and combination were filmed on the roof. Emmett's
dream was to someday parachute into the Brazilian jungle
to make a film of the mating habits of the headhunters,
whom he claimed had forty-five minute orgasms. His one
other attempt at an on-location foreign film had been
abortive. On two consecutive days he had been arrested

for shoplifting large quantities of costume jewelry. Each time he told the police that he needed the jewelry to trade for hashish in Tangiers. No charges were ever pressed.

When he took over the additional floor it was a warren of rubbish. Rather than have it carted away, he ran the elevator down to the basement, cut the cables, and pushed the junk down after it. In addition to the usual bottles, tin cans, coffee containers, newspapers and toilet-paper roll cores by the hundreds, there was every variety of cardboard box, plaster lathe and sheetrock, plus a broken piano. Also thirty-seven years of invoices and canceled checks of a printing firm and thirteen cherrywood cases of movable type. Two flights up in the shaftway, on top of the pile, were four huge cast-iron radiators. The building had once had steam heat, but when the boiler cracked and went two seasons without repair, the tenants, who were all artists of one sort or another, installed their own gas space heaters.

It's a simple matter to bypass a ConEd gas meter with piping so as not to have to pay for clean, modern, dependable gas heat. But then you always have to worry about a meter reader spotting you on the stairs someday. Many artists prefer the method of taking the meter off one night a month and turning it back with a vacuum cleaner attached to the input connection of the meter. There's a store two blocks down on Canal Street, one of those with display cases on casters that they push out onto the sidewalk in the daytime, which sells wide silver-colored tape for thirty-nine cents a roll that's ideal for making an airtight seal between gas meter and vacuum cleaner. Anyway, Emmett had pushed the old radiators, which weighed about six hundred pounds apiece, into the shaft last to pack the rest of the debris down tight.

The only tenants to complain about the loss of the elevator were an environmental painter named Bent and an opportunistic rock-group promoter who liked to be called S.S. All of Bent's paintings resembled huge vulvas and he took the filling of the elevator shaft as a gross insult to his art and threatened to castrate Emmett. Bent's daddy in Amarillo cut off his allowance and S.S. got mugged by some Grand Street toughs who took umbrage at his tight pants. As a result, he lost an eye, for which he had his mother embroider a psychedelic Day-Glo eye patch. He and Bent moved to London, where they founded a successful design firm specializing in plastic interiors for jetliners.

Emmett framed out the hole and put down flooring in what had been the shaftway on each of his two floors. He lived on the lower level in the area between the entrance door and where the elevator had been. The rest of that floor was for moviemaking. As his films received increasing recognition, he found that he needed more space so he cut out the flooring and joists of his upper floor, giving him a two-story sound stage. He left a two-foot-wide perimeter on three sides of the old floor so he could get to the windows in the summer. He loved the idea of a huge hole that was all his. From the outside nobody could tell that Emmett had this hole, or that the building was now structurally unsound. In the area directly above where he slept he left the floor intact and it was here that he stored his cacti over the winter. He used some of the leftover wood for the floor in the shaftway. The remainder, heavy four-inch by sixteen-inch joist timbers, went to the ground-floor poet, Lee.

Lee was an excellent imitator of all that was worst in Blake, only he tried to be snider. He affected exotic clothing, hoping to conceal his midwestern lack of imagination. He had lived in Kyoto for a year and seven months, and if nothing else, had noticed the architecture. The ground floor, like most loft buildings, had a much higher ceiling than the upper stories. Using the leftover four-inch by sixteen-inch timbers, Lee had a carpenter build a rugged platform and steps up to it, creating a second level of existence.

Directly above Lee lived two queens who ran a dance-book store in the East Sixties. They never troubled anybody in the building and were very domestic. Once a year they would give a screaming party. At this year's party, celebrating the one hundred thirteenth anniversary of Oscar Wilde's birth, two muscle-magazine beauties tried to fuck in the bathtub. It was one of those rococo affairs with claw-and-ball feet. Two of the tub's legs cracked off and the drainpipe pulled loose, flooding Lee's loft and sending him scrambling up on his ledge.

Anyway, we needed a sink light enough for two men to carry up a cramped staircase seven flights, actually six and a stoop, and that fit the description of the sink I had bought the preceding Sunday which had never been delivered. I am a very physical person and don't mind work, but my time was limited. In fact, I am a compulsive worker. But I hate to be told what to do or when. That's why I don't work in a shop anymore and now build lofts

for artists and people who like to live like artists with
lots of room and light, but comfortably. I'm not knocking comfort. I live alone on the Lower East Side in an
apartment, actually the whole floor of a building as big as
a loft, with just my Doberman bitch, who guards my tools
when I'm out drinking at Max's Kansas City. I get a lot
of my work through Max's. I'm a perpetual college drop-
out. In the fourteen years since I graduated from high
school I've been in and out of four colleges and never
gotten a bachelor's. Several years ago I quit my job as a
shop foreman to go back to school. I was a lousy foreman because when the work didn't get done or one of
the mechanics couldn't do it right, I'd do it myself. I was
the only foreman in the trade who didn't sit on his ass
all day and drink coffee. Any mechanic who worked in
my shop figured it was the best job he ever had. As a
result, I was the grimiest foreman in all of N.Y.C.
, Anyway, I went back to school and started drinking in
Max's, where they serve free fried chicken legs and wings,
meat balls, and occasionally chipped beef from 5:00 to
7:00 P.M. every weekday. Richard Solomon Levi, the only
poet ever to have a reader's contract with *The New
Yorker* at age twenty, used to eat the free chicken at
Max's every day with me and we played a reverse form of
the dozens. One of us would spot a good-looking girl
alone at the bar and start by urging the other to pick her
up. Interest in the girl would be secondary to how inventive we could make our persuasions. What had to remain
unstated was that we each knew either of us could have
her; it was a sort of *noblesse oblige*. He started to dwindle
and finally a doctor told him that he would get cancer

from eating nothing but free chicken. It turns out that restaurant chickens are raised on chemicals. From the *Times,* with no by-line:

MRS. GRANT REITERATES CITY STAND ON CHICKENS

Mrs. Bess Myerson Grant, the City's Commissioner of Consumer Affairs, held a news conference in a Long Island City poultry terminal yesterday to announce a "new" department regulation that, in fact, has been department procedure for many years.

Mrs. Grant said that from now on her department's inspectors would not allow on the market hikens with cancerous tumors. Then, under questioning, Mrs. Grant said that the inspectors had not knowingly allowed such chickens to pass inspection in the past either.

The purpose of her announcement was not entirely clear, although it was apparently designed to call attention to lobbying by the chicken industry.

It bothered him to eat the meat balls and chipped beef, which were both immersed in a sauce like thin ketchup. He had a heroic beard, which helped him get modeling jobs as a spear carrier, and the gravy made problems maintaining his dignity.

Several of the bartenders at Max's are painters and they all live in lofts. I started converting their lofts to raise some money while I was still in school. I don't want to die of free chicken cancer either. Max's is an artist's bar much like the old Cedars, but with microskirted waitresses and bigger drinks. The bartenders recommended me for carpentry and plumbing jobs. Soon I quit school again and now I only build lofts.

I'm a tool freak and most of the money I make goes into buying more tools that enable me to work faster and easier and make more money. You can't own anything pawnable on the Lower East Side and keep it for long unless you structure your life to protect your possessions from the local amphetamine-head burglars. This I do to a great extent, but when I must go out, the Doberman, who is extremely possessive, looks after my material world. The problem is that she also intrudes on my other world. She refuses to let me bring home Max's microskirted waitresses whenever she is in heat. This interference in my sex life only makes me build more lofts.

I almost always work alone in a loft, locking the door and dreading fire and building inspectors. Almost all lofts are illegal to live in. This leads to all kinds of paranoia for those who live in them. Like where do you throw your garbage and why are you walking down a street zoned for heavy manufacturing at 4:00 A.M. This same paranoia affects the unlicensed plumbers and electricians who convert lofts into living space for artists. It is probably good for the artists, making them constantly aware of their alienation from their environment and its official-dom. For me, it makes me work very fast.

The architect's loft was taking much longer than I had expected. I had to finish it fast to get paid in time to cash the check by 3:00 P.M. Friday so I would have money for Christmas shopping. On the preceding Sunday I had gone to a secondhand refrigerator place on Second Avenue. I had never dealt with this particular dealer before. I bought a gas range, a bathtub, a refrigerator, a hot-water heater, and a forty-two-inch pressed-steel combination kitchen tub and sink with base cabinet and sliding drainboard, all to be delivered no later than noon on Monday. I figured that way I would have them by Wednesday, if the dealer was as predictable as most. Usually after placing an order it takes half a dozen phone calls and/or trips to his shop to get delivery. This dealer promised everything would be different from now on and I promised to buy lots of sinks. He swore the sink would look like brand-new. He couldn't take me to see it but it would be there on Monday. I inspected all my other purchases then and there. Monday I spent framing out the work, cutting and threading my pipe and pulling out the worst of the old toilets. Old manufacturing lofts all have at least two toilets. I take one out and that leaves a ready-made drainline connection for the new sink and bathtub. Tuesday everything but the sink arrived. By 4:30 P.M. Wednesday the job was completed except for connecting the tub and sink.

I don't own a car, so I borrowed my friend Sam's and drove to Second Avenue. The dealer I had bought the sink from had had a different excuse each time I had

called, and as much as I envied his imagination, push had
finally come to shove. This time he said that he was going
to Pitt Street in a few minutes to get the sink. I said that
I would follow and put it right into Sam's stationwagon
and deliver it myself. The dealer said that would be impossible, I would have to wait at his shop, and proudly
explained the circumstances. Whenever he needs sinks, he
has an arrangement with the super of a housing project.
The super pulls out good sinks, condemns them as scrap,
and buys new ones. The dealer sells the project new sinks
and buys back the slightly used ones. The city pays for
the scam. It's the same device parking garages use. They
have one burned-out headlight bulb. Each day they install it in a different car, removing a good one. When the
customer returns, the attendant tells him that he has
safety-checked the car and found one headlight out. The
garage can't lose. It either sells a new bulb, actually the
used one removed earlier, or if the owner refuses, they
are at least ahead one made-new bulb.

The dealer came back without the sink. The project
custodial staff was having a Christmas party and he'd have
to go back the next day, when fewer people would be
around. The next two days the super was too busy making all the repairs he had avoided for the last three
months so he could coerce the tenants into giving him
Christmas tips.

By Friday I was coerced enough to borrow Sam and his
car again. Sam is a professor of classics at a girls' college
and on vacation at this time of year. He plans to move
into a loft soon and I will convert it for him for free. In
barter he is going to teach me ancient Greek. He has the

most wide-ranging verbal intelligence I have ever en-
countered. He knows so much and thinks so fast he has
trouble keeping track of his thoughts—as a consequence
he yells a lot. He is a nonacademic poet who tends toward
a very personal shorthand in order to capture his ideas.
As a result, his poems are so laconic few people can follow
them. His twelve-year-old son, Ezra, took great delight at
my increasing agitation during the week, declaring at
every opportunity that I had everything but the kitchen
sink. Children are a great source of solace at such times.
Other peoples'.

I borrowed enough money from Sam to buy a second
secondhand sink. The dealer was at his sister's funeral
and wouldn't be back to the shop until 1:00 P.M., so I
couldn't get a refund until then. I finally found what I
needed on Seventh Avenue. The right side of the base
cabinet was rusted through, but that side went against the
wall and wouldn't show. As we drove downtown, Sam
kept talking about going to the bus terminal to watch the
people trying to get home for the holidays, knowing that
they would arrive late, only to have to leave early. All I
could think of was a line in William Bolitho's book *Mur-
der for Profit,* that invariably all mass murderers had at
one time in their lives been in the secondhand-goods
business.

THE AVENUE B BUS LINE

THE AVENUE B and East Broadway Coach Company is the last franchised private bus line operating in Manhattan. As a result, the Avenue B buses are the only ones that run on schedule—every four minutes until 7:00 P.M. and then every nine minutes until 1:00 A.M. After that they run only once every hour until dawn. There are three separate north-south routes going to the Civic Center, Chinatown, and the Lower East Side. Above Grand Street, where there is a free transfer to an east-west shuttle bus, the three lines converge and run on Clinton Street, which becomes Avenue B, and then crosstown on Fourteenth Street terminating at Fifteenth Street and Fourth Avenue, between Klein's main store and Annex, and just two blocks south of Max's Kansas City.

It was an early Sunday morning as I waited on Avenue B for the bus to take me from Seventh Street up to Max's for the last softball game of the season. There is a tradition in N.Y.C. for artists' and writers' bars to sponsor ballteams of misfits and malcontents in order to keep them in shape so that their sedentary work doesn't let them physically deteriorate to the point where they lose interest in drinking. Of course, at Max's, unlike the old Cedar Street Tavern, there are always the waitresses to keep the regulars coming back. But not at ten in the morning on a Sunday.

In my years-long romance with the Avenue B bus line both the vehicles themselves and their riders have remained of undiminishing fascination to me, my interest has increasingly been taking on all the fanaticism of a steam-railroad buff. A few months ago I realized that I was learning to identify the various individual coaches by their numbers. They all have prominently displayed three-digit numbers. City-owned buses have four digits and are painted a drab two-tone green. Avenue B buses are red and yellow. There is one bus, #308, the oldest one on the line, that in addition to the large posted notices that all buses must carry prohibiting smoking, spitting, and standing forward of the line, has a decaying paper notice framed under glass quoting from the franchise agreement to the effect that when the outside temperature falls below 55°F., they will supply heat on all enclosed coaches, but that they are not required to supply heat to the open upper level of double-deck coaches. It is quite hard to read because of both the yellowing paper and the fly specking. The last time I rode on an open bus was in the late forties, and besides, that was on Fifth Avenue. That was when O'Dwyer was mayor. Bill O'Dwyer, the only mayor of an American city who ever had to flee to

Mexico while still in office, not Paul, his younger, gentler
brother. A few years later N.Y.C. bought the Fifth Avenue Coach Lines with the aid of Roy Cohn, and there
were no more double-deckers. Possibly what really en-
dears the Avenue B buses to me is the notice you first see
when boarding, posted just behind the driver, stating that
no more than two policemen will be carried free of
charge on any given bus and then only if they are in full
uniform.

The passengers, too, seem to be of a more human sort.
Charles Olson in *The Mayan Letters* writes of his surprise
at his own pleasure at being so jammed into a bus in
rural Mexico that his traditional North American need
for privacy and presumed dignity was superfluous. Unlike
Olson's Mexican bus, the Avenue B buses carry no chickens. They remain in Sara Delano Roosevelt Park and on
the fire escapes along Forsyth Street while their owners
take the Avenue B buses to work.

Just before rush hour in the afternoon is my favorite
time to ride. I once sat behind a lady freshly emerged
from Klein's as she systematically sorted out the cosmetics
she had just shoplifted. She took out each item, examined
it closely and then either put it back into another compartment of her large oilskin bag or set it aside. She
looked like a schoolteacher in her late forties and wore no
makeup at all, but she did have plucked eyebrows. Apparently I violated our trust by watching her too closely, as
she suddenly pulled the bell cord and got off before she
had been able to completely sort out her take. Whatever
she didn't keep was neatly stowed on the seat for whom-
ever found and desired them. There seemed to be no

particular pattern as to what brand of cosmetics she kept, but each choice was the most garishly colored of its type. As I watched her, I began to understand my ex-wife better. Whenever we visited anyone's house, she would immediately excuse herself to the bathroom, where she would examine their medicine cabinet, reporting its contents to me at the first propitious moment, with what at the time seemed to me to be an encyclopedic recall.

Anyway, by the time I got to Max's that morning most of the team was there. I started talking to Rus, who had been reading the second-section feature story in the *Times* about the fruit auctions moving from the Washington Street Market to the new terminal at Hunt's Point. The auctioneer was displaying limes to the reporter, explaining that although large, wrinkled limes had more juice (not true—but the reporter didn't know this), the retailers in Jewish neighborhoods were buying smaller, smoother-skinned ones that day as that was what their clientele preferred. It seemed to make as much sense as anything else on a Sunday morning as we drank black coffee and tried to remember if anyone had scored the night before. It would soon enough be apparent by who failed to show for the game. Even a rational man will get up with a hangover to play baseball, but no man in his right mind would if he had someone to make his coffee for him without his getting up, and even better if there was also a Bloody Mary with lots of bitters. The S.L.A. being what it is and this being too early on a Sunday, we were drinking coffee.

Rus is a very quiet man, younger than most of the writers around Max's, and has a very literal approach to his

own life. He claims that there were only two determinants
in his life. First, while he was still in high school, he had
read D. H. Lawrence's *Aaron's Rod* and couldn't shake
the cynicism of the scene where Aaron for the first time
felt carefree in the midst of a celebrating crowd, even
enjoying its crush, only to later discover that his wallet
had been lifted. Some years later in college Rus had seen
an old movie on television in which Edward G. Robinson
played a policeman who was defrocked because of his
scrupulous honesty. Robinson defined a friend as someone
who pats you on the back to see where it will most easily
break.

Rus tired of the *Times* and started talking about an
essay he had just read in the literary magazine *Kulchur,*
by the poet George Oppen. In it Oppen said that when
the battle lines are drawn between Bohemia and Philistia,
there is never a frontal assault, rather that they both snipe
at the artist. Oppen was a tool and die maker by trade
before he retired, which may account for much of my
respect for his precise poetry. He once told me the story
of a lunch conversation he had with an old tool maker
when they both worked in the Hudson auto factory in
Detroit. Even at lunch hour in a tool shop each man's
trade is immediately apparent. The welders simply dump
out their sandwiches on the workbench and eat. The
mechanics wash their hands first and then complain about
the same old thing. The tool and die maker folds back his
cuffs, washes up, spreads out the wax paper on each sandwich and looks to see what he has. Then he goes to his
wooden toolbox with its felt-lined drawers and takes out a
steel ruler, slices each sandwich corner to corner, wipes

off the ruler with an oiled rag, and replaces it in its proper drawer. Then he sits down to eat. I was once accused of being un-American over lunch. A mechanic, a recent immigrant from Calabria, watched me intently after lunch as I folded up the aluminum foil my sandwiches had been wrapped in and put it back on the shelf in my locker. He told me I would destroy America if I did that. A very perceptive mechanic, but he will never be a tool maker. The old Austrian was telling George, who was then still a young man, about his wedding to an American girl. After telling of the reception he skipped to the morning after. He had gotten up first and started to make the coffee. His bride, still in bed, called out would he mind making breakfast since he was already up. The Austrian made it clear to George that he immediately realized that this could be a crucial deciding point in the course of his marriage. He asked George what he would have done. The older man then whispered that he had cut the grapefruit in the wrong direction. George and he both knew that if it had been a welder, he probably would have smashed something. George still wonders if the wife even noticed.

Paul and Julie came over to our booth to look at the paper. On and off I have worked with both of them when I have had a job that was too much for one man to handle. I no longer work in a shop and now build lofts for artists. Paul is the son of a Brooklyn hackie turned truck farmer. When he had been little, his father, who drove seven nights a week, would give Paul his full change dispenser on weekends and send him off to Coney Island. This gave Paul a great sense of independence at a young

age and produced lots of younger brothers and sisters. As
he tired of Coney Island, he would wander over to Sheeps-
head Bay and watch the charter boats come in. Sometimes there would be a single tuna so big that the
fisherman would hire a local kid to get the use of his Red
Flyer wagon to carry the fish home.

After they moved to Long Island, the family survived
the Depression raising vegetables to sell in Chinatown.
Paul, who had never cared much for school, spent most
of his time on the shore playing hookey. One day he got
angry at some other children who invaded his shore, so
he packed their ears full of sand. After that the authorities were just as happy if he didn't come to school. There
was a channel dredged in the bay where barges carrying
heating oil for the suburban homes came in. The barge
captains taught Paul to watch for the change in the rip-
ples on the surface of the oily water so he would know
exactly where to cast his line so it would drop right into
the channel and down to the eels that lived there. As he
grew older he started working the clam boats that went
further east on the North Shore. Realizing that he would
never make enough to buy his own boat that way he
joined the crew of a night oyster boat. They would sneak
into the private, seeded oyster beds where they could steal
several hundred dollars' worth in one night. Although
this could result in several years in jail the only way they
could be successfully prosecuted was if the Nassau County
Police caught them while they were still on the beds. The
oyster crew got some nitromethanol from some hot-
rodders who used it as fuel in specially prepared engines
at the local P.A.L.-sponsored drag strip. They put it in

the fuel tank of the police boat. The next time out the
old flat-head inboard motor in the police launch blew up,
caving in the lapstreak hull. By the time the police raised
the scuttled launch and repaired her, Paul had saved
enough money for his own boat and quit stealing oysters.

He clammed all along the North Shore for some years.
As the pollution made more and more areas unusable, the
competition became so intense that one day he found
painted on his boat, "If you can't eat them, why do you
dig them." Not wishing to have nitro slipped into his gas
tanks, he shifted from clamming to fishing, which meant
bringing his catch to Fulton Street instead of selling it
locally. The first night he came into Max's it was about
1:00 A.M. He started rapping on a waitress who told him
that she didn't get off until 4:00 A.M., which was true,
figuring that by that time he would either be too drunk
or have gone home. At 3:00 A.M. he was at the Fulton
Street fish market and got back to Max's just in time for
last call. The waitress was so surprised to see him back
she ran up to the office and made Tony Gould, who was
then the manager, escort her into a cab. Paul soon got a
loft in N.Y.C. and I put in a shower for him first thing.
He now works as a stone mason but changes jobs often.
Being a graphic artist well founded in draftsmanship, it
is easy for him to read a blueprint. There is nothing that
galls a foreman more than a journeyman looking at the
prints and possibly seeing something recognizable. Louis
Zukofsky says somewhere that education costs us the ability to earn a living easily. Paul is learning to act craftily
stupid on the job.

About six months ago Paul decided to try fishing again,

this time crabbing in Chesapeake Bay. On his way down
he stopped at Marlboro, Maryland, at a seafood shack
just across from the racetrack and ordered crabs. They
came out minced and stuffed into horrid little crab-shaped
red plastic serving dishes that looked like a child's floating
bathtub soap-dispensing toy. He came back to N.Y.C.
that same night.

Julie, who came in with Paul, is the strongest man I've
ever met. When he was in high school, the alley owner
used to make him use an eleven-pound cork bowling ball
so he wouldn't break up the place. When he got out of
high school he started to work for a safe company. Usually when they sold a new fire-rated vault, they would
take an old cast-iron safe in on trade, which they then
sold to a scrap-metal dealer. To keep these old safes from
being resold in competition with their new ones by the
scrap dealer, they would literally crack the cast-iron doors,
often up to eight inches thick. This was done with a
twenty-two-pound sledge hammer. That was Julie's first
job.

To better order his life and to develop absolute muscu-
lar control Julie started to study yoga by himself. Within
months he progressed to where he could internally cleanse
himself with a string. This was done by introducing one
end of a ball of twine through a nostril and by will drawing it through the entire alimentary canal and finally ex-
pelling it. He then sought the aid of a yoga master to
guide him to even further self-mastery. The yogi offered
to tutor him for no charge if Julie would tell the yogi's
other students that he, the master, had taught Julie.

Julie was so disillusioned at the idea of pandering for a master that he quit yoga and became a weight lifter. He went back to school and is now an electromicroscopist specializing in marine biology.

Lee, a poet I had done some minor work for once, came into the bar. He is neither a Max's regular nor on the ballteam, but he wanted to see me and Paul about some work. He is the only poet in N.Y.C. who has a literary agent. The agent, who had no idea of how to market a four-hundred-seventy-two-page poetry manuscript, entitled *The Flagellant's Goat,* by an unknown poet, went to a publishing house that hasn't published any new verse since Thomas Hardy's day. They accepted it, apparently feeling that it couldn't fail to impress upon the N.B.A. judges that they were still in business. With an advance of $3,200, Lee now wanted to install a modern suburban kitchen and bath in his loft. Lee left as soon as it was agreed that I would meet him the next day to estimate the plumbing and Paul to estimate the tile and marble work. Lee is the last male in a long line of Protestant ministers. He was raised by his mother and four spinster aunts after his father fled to Alaska. Some years ago the commercial salmon fisherman discovered (it later proved to be erroneous) that the Dolly Varden trout ate salmon eggs. They instituted a bounty on Dolly Vardens, one dollar in gold, cash on delivery, for every forty trout tails strung on a wire. Lee's father caught, chopped up, and strung onto wire at least as many salmon as he did Dolly Vardens, but the town needed a preacher and it was cheaper to pay him for tails than to give him a salary.

Lee himself hasn't had such good luck with fish. His first wife gave him a piranha for Christmas one year. He would go uptown to Macy's three times a week to buy an eleven-cent goldfish for its dinner. It was a very perverse fish, attacking the goldfish only after all the lights were out at night, and then only from the rear. Every other morning Lee would find the head and front third of the goldfish floating on the surface and the piranha sedentary on the bottom of the tank digesting. During the subway strike a few years ago Lee couldn't get to Macy's and, having no suitable food in the house, he went to a neighborhood German delicatessen and bought one slice of liverwurst, which he fed to his fish. The next morning all the liverwurst was gone and the piranha was floating on the surface, all its coloration faded, and dead. As soon as the subway strike ended, Lee took up a macrobiotic diet. Gary Snyder has pointed out that the macrobiotic foods of North America are venison, apples, maize and acorns. Lee ate only brown rice and dried fish.

Lee's second wife was Carla, an ex-teenie-bopper-motorcyclist. She had once been the most famous garage groupie in N.Y.C. She had read the introduction to *Human Sexual Response* and had started taking up with mechanics, seeking one to duplicate The Machine. She married Lee after hearing him referred to as a mechanistic poet, and they both sought their fulfillment in Scientology. She soon contracted hepatitis and Lee went on alone to England to be cleared. His auditor revealed to him the sublime truth that all poetry is tautology. Lee was reborn. In his joy at his own rebirth, minus the little two-inch-

tall thetans running around inside his head, he wrote his
first clear poem.

FEET OF CLAY

ya' know
my
father once told
me
"a fool's a
mule"
ya' know
why because
he's
stuborn

Lee returned to America full of profound joy and wis-
dom and complacency only to find the talk was of
revolution. Lee had once edited a U.S.I.S.- and C.I.A.-
sponsored house organ in Peru and had a slight knowledge
of Spanish. With this insight he was soon a full-fledged
closet revolutionary. He founded a new magazine of revo-
lutionary poetry and thought called *Gusano*. Somehow
Lee's sense of confrontation has always seemed to me to be
like the bridge across the Susquehanna River at Harrisburg, Pennsylvania. At the time the bridge was built,
Harrisburg prided itself as the "Gateway to the West."
Lining both sides of the bridge every fifty feet or so are
poles topped by American eagles, every one of which faces
the westward-bound adventurer. Returning to the East
you are confronted by a mass of eagles' asses.

Lee hired Richard Solomon Levi as the correspondent to cover Central and South America. Levi was to ride on trains until his train was stopped by revolutionaries. He was then to reveal his true identity and attempt to join Ché in the hills. Levi got as far as Acapulco, where he was detained under house arrest pending the final disposition of a wealthy North American lady's divorce case. This occurred while he was trying to raise funds for his train tickets south. When Levi was released, he financed his plane fare back to New York City by buying cheap clay piggy banks, cramming them full of Dexadrine (no prescription being required in Mexico), covering the piggy banks with papier-mâché, painting them to look like piñata pigs and mailing them to various friends in the U.S. Soon a first-class ticket was cabled to him. He now works at Idlewild as a cooper installing banding iron on luggage that customs agents have perished in their zeal.

Meanwhile, most of the softball team had arrived and we set out for New City. On the way there Paul told me about his new neighbor, a film maker named Emmett, who had lived in the same building as Lee but who had had an argument with his landlady and had been forced to move. Emmett has an extensive reputation for making underground shorts and was now seeking financial backing for a feature movie. It is to be a remake of *I Shoot for the Stars,* for which he hopes to sign Marlene Dietrich as the young Wernher Von Braun and John Wayne as the first experimental V-2 rocket. No contracts or options have been signed yet.

When we got to the house in New City where Mike, his wife, and their six children live summers, we met the

local team and drove to the town park. Mike is a minimal
sculptor and feature-story editor for the *Post*. About 1959
N.Y.C. apparently felt that the way to keep the Fire Department happy without giving them a pay raise was to let
them harass artists living in lofts. Mike conned the *Post*
into running one of its dandy ten-part features on the
artists' life-style. The reporters seemed sympathetic but
uncomprehending. The first installment ended with a
statement by the abstract expressionist Basil King, "My
wife needn't take an aeroplane to the supermarket." The
art critic from the *Times* was incensed at the presumption
of the *Post* to write about Art (which it didn't) . In re-
buttal he wrote that the expressionists would do well to
lead domestic apartment lives and anyway their paintings
would then of necessity be of more handy dimensions. A
year or two later the world was given soup cans. Obviously the *Times* is more prescient than even it dares take
credit. It was after this that Mike moved to a loft on the
second floor of a building on the corner of Broadway and
Spring Street. Left over from the previous tenant, a fabric
house, in gold leaf on the corner window there is still a
sign which from the street reads "RAYON AND
PUERTO RICAN UNDERWEAR." To this day none
of us has been able to interpret that, but the possibilities
exhaust the nonmercantile mind. Mike needed quite a bit
of carpentry done to build sleeping platforms for the
whole family. Julie and I agreed to do the job, which
actually took longer than we had originally planned. The
lumber and masonite were delivered in the morning on
schedule. We figured to work nights because of Julie's
full-time job. For two weeks Mike kept delaying us while

he arranged the uncut four-foot by eight-foot sheets of masonite and the sixteen-foot lengths of two-by-fours into floor sculptures and then had a photographer from his paper take pictures, which he took around to the galleries. They fit the market's new fancy. That's how Mike bought his house in New City.

The ballgame was a fiasco. Max's lost 22–20 after getting eight runs in the top of the first.

After the game we went back to Mike's house and Sam offered to take charge of barbecuing the steaks which Max's had supplied. Sam is a classicist of limited cooking skill who survives quite well in the world of New England academic classicists, most of whom are émigré gourmets. He makes a ritual of the timing of simple foods, e.g., the vegetables are to be picked only after the wine is uncorked. A typical meal at Sam's would be: raw asparagus and red bell-pepper salad (possibly with a bit of red cabbage), beef marrow on homemade black bread, and golden bantam corn picked after the water is at a rolling boil. The guests bring the table wines.

Sam's wife was just as happy to see him doing the cooking, figuring that would leave little opportunity for him to letch after the waitresses from Max's who had come along to watch the game. She has never been able to understand that Sam is true to her by choice and, like Li Po, is more likely to drown while drunkenly attempting to make love to the moon's reflection in the river than he is to run off with another woman. Sam has published two books, one of verse, the other a really inventive pornographic novel written to pay for their summer vacation.

Both books have had the same one-word title, his wife's
Christian name.

After the party we all got back to the city without mis-
hap and reassembled at Max's. Now, without exception
Max's microskirted waitresses are pretty. This may in part
be an illusion created by the dim lighting. But the undis-
puted sweetheart is a girl named Pat. She may not be
the most beautiful woman I've ever seen, but more than
once I've noticed her standing off to herself, by the glassware rack at the end of the service bar, doing a sort of
half-dance half-shuffle, mumbling along to Janis Joplin's
song "Down on Me"; she turned on every man at the bar
—oblivious to what she had done. She is strangely affected by music. About three years ago, when soul music
was first getting onto hip white jukeboxes, she said one
night about Aretha Franklin's record of "Respect," "Oh,
but that's a social-protest song." It may just be that her
sense of humor is beyond me. Possibly inspired by the
salad servers at work, she once designed a pair of cupped
tongs mounted on the end of a pantograph which she
marketed to poodle-owning fags as pristine shit-pickers.
She made quite a bit of money while the device was in
vogue, but lost it all on the stock market by following the
advice of an astrologic investment-counseling service in
Minnesota. She now designs miniature cloisonné lapel
emblems for all the *ad hoc* radical political-activist com-
mittees. Pat left alone, as always, it's probably just as well.
I could never really be attracted to a woman who doesn't
have pierced ears.

I left soon after and walked down to Fifteenth Street

to catch my bus. Sitting on the bench installed by the
savings bank on the corner, I began to think about all
the events of my day in the country and about the de-
humanizing effects of the city. As #308 pulled in I was
trying to remember Juan Belmonte's exact words in his
autobiography contrasting his home with N.Y.C., which
he found so confusing with its streets called only by letters and numbers.

PREMIERE – NO SHIT

I CAN DATE it exactly, Memorial Day 1967, the last time I had been called a beatnik. On that holiday N.Y.C. had its first undisguised police riot (for several years now the few black militants I know, who still talk to me, have defined what the newspapers call a "riot" as the police chasing people through the streets). In May 1967 I saw it firsthand, and by September 1968 what had happened a year and a half before in N.Y.C. was institutionalized in Chicago, and I no longer had to justify my paranoia. The grounds keeper in Tompkins Square Park, in what is euphemistically called the East Village, got agitated at seeing some hippies sitting on the grass (a misdemeanor by Parks Department regulations) and called the cops.

The precinct commander for the Ninth is really, no shit, named Captain (now Deputy Inspector) Fink. He is considered by many to be the most thoughtful, shrewd

and sympathetic senior officer on the entire force. But
even a cop with a background in sociology needs an occasional day off from overseeing the precinct with the
highest rates of both burglary and crimes of violence in
the entire city. The Ninth Precinct is a gerrymandered
district running roughly from the East River to The
Bowery and from Delancey Street up to Fourteenth
Street, with little pockets of relative affluence carved out
along its borders. When the now defunct *New York
Herald Tribune* was struggling towards its end, it ran a
series of articles called "City in Crisis" (it is no accident
that only a newspaper that knew it was going under had
the balls to write the truth, the same *Herald Tribune*
that got Jack Kennedy so uptight that he had it banned
from the White House over their coverage of his mis-
handling of Cuba). "City in Crisis" was possibly the best
newspaper writing, that is, committed to a love of its subject, since Leibling. A good argument can be made that
the true decline of N.Y.C. is directly attributable to the
deaths of A. J. and the *Trib*. In March 1969 Governor
Rockefeller rammed through the Republican State Legislature a bill cutting welfare payments to sixty-six cents
per day per person for food, on the same day the figures
came out that for the twenty-second consecutive month
the cost of living went up half of one percent. Five years
ago "City in Crisis" ran a multipart article on welfare
that was the beginning of the gradual welfare reforms
that Rockefeller ended. It was "City in Crisis" that first
named St. Marks Place between Third and Second Avenues "The Hub of the Hip" and then revealed to all

but the Ninth's residents that they had a higher rate of violent crimes than either Red Hook or Harlem.

After the *Tribune* folded, the closest thing to a concerned newspaper that N.Y.C. had was *EVO* (the *East Village Other*), which for all its lack of copy editing, at least for its first year or two before it became drug-disoriented, gave a flying fuck for its resident readers. *EVO*'s weekly issue following its very own neighborhood police riot had the most telling photographs of all the New York papers and an impassioned story drawing an analogy with the Washington Square Park police busts of folksingers and listeners of ten years earlier in the West Village as the first step in cleaning up the area for the real-estate developers who tore down the nineteenth-century wood and brick buildings to put up façadeless high-rise upper-middle-income apartment houses. It seems quaint now to think that the concerned voice at the time thought that all "they" wanted to do was clear out the undesirables to make room for rent gouging, but that was when strangers still smiled at you in the streets and before the Maf realized that the acid that those smiling young girls were tripping on could be cut with methedrine and real money was to be made.

That was also before I became known as a hippie instead of a beatnik at the Chit-Chat Tavern. That was also before Tony Bud got his face shot off. The Chit-Chat is a bar directly across the street from the building where I live on Seventh Street between Avenues B and C, and for three or four years I would stop in there for one drink a day, just to keep my hand in. I was the only

drinker there who was not a member of the Ukrainian
local of the house-wreckers union. I had started drinking
there while I was renovating my building nights (still
working days in the garage). They could watch me
through the lit windows and speculate (I found out later)
on my demon. On the day that the work on the house
was completed and the Certificate of Occupancy secured
I went into the Chit-Chat and announced to Tony that
I wasn't going to do another damned thing on that building for six months. Tony just laughed and bought me a
drink (the only free drink I ever saw in that place),
knowing more than I did at the time, that I'd be back at
work the next Saturday. Tony was the only reason that
the house wreckers tolerated me. House wreckers are the
lowest-paid of all the construction trades and theirs was
the only union until quite recently that even begrudg-
ingly admitted black members—in a separate local.
Ukrainian wreckers are the only construction workers
who drink more than riggers. They rarely work more
than two or three days in any given week. Riggers go to
work, drunk or not, with the result that almost every construction fatality is caused by some rigger who couldn't
steady a guy rope. Wreckers have enough sense not to go
in when they don't feel up to it, since they, unlike riggers,
would be endangering their own lives. For a long time I
deluded myself that the reason that I was tolerated by the
wreckers was that they used to see me working so hard
across the street, but of course it was my hair. That and
their interest in my sex life. Every time I got some nooky,
the next day I'd hear, "So the blonde with the Connecticut plates on her V.W. stayed over last night, huh!" or

the like. Nobody drinks in the Chit-Chat by choice. The wreckers drink there because Jack-the-Pollack, the president of their local, tells them to. It is the collection point for Iggy, the official union loan shark. Iggy drives a blue Cadillac (on the Lower East Side all sharks, bookies, bar owners and G.P.'s must drive Cadillacs) registered in Florida with a black vinyl top and a plaque in lieu of a front license plate that says "Miami Beach Sheriff's Office" (of course, there is no Miami Beach Sheriff's Office, the name of the municipality being Dade County, but nobody ever says anything to Iggy about that). He wears a pinky ring on each hand and has a white miniature poodle named Martini (a drink like any other mixed drink, other than rye and either soda or Coke, that is unobtainable at the Chit-Chat) and has never been known to fuck a woman. Which is not to say that Iggy doesn't have girl friends. His latest is Amy, wife of the local mountain spring-water vendor, whom he takes to Miami Beach once every year for two weeks. Iggy only likes his girls to give him head, but the greatest pleasure he gets is having everybody know it. It has never occurred to anyone to ask Iggy what he does for his ladies, or not in his presence. A wrecker would as soon fall off a six-story demolition job as admit to having eaten pussy.

Not being an activist, and seeing what was happening in the park that Memorial Day, I split and went to the Chit-Chat to get a shot of Harper's (don't even try to get a Tennessee bourbon there, it was only with some trouble that I got them to keep a bottle of Harper's, before that the best in the house was Old Grand-Dad 86, not Grand-Dad 100, which is bonded). As usual one of the regulars

called out, "Here comes that beatnick" (a fitting term in
the origin of both the speaker and the suffix, dating as it
does from the first Russian sputnik in 1957, the year
Kerouac, Corso and Ginsberg arrived back in N.Y.C.) .
The next morning's *New York Daily News* called the
"rioters" "hippies" and from then on I was the house
hippie to the Chit-Chat. They have both always struck
me as misnomers in that both hippies and beatniks have
enough sense not to work, a sanity I have yet to achieve.
By way of the relative truth of the name of the *New York
Daily News,* let me quote in its entirety the following
story:

Keeps Valet in Car Trunk

Durban, South Africa, March
30 (Reuters)—An African servant whose employer carries
him around in the closed trunk
of his car is looking for another job.

The employer, Canadian immigrant Frank Thompson, told
newsmen last week : "I always
take him in the trunk—that's
his place."

The African said today he
had been offered several jobs
after neighbors complained to
a local newspaper about the
practise. He said he earned
about $11 a month.

Thompson's comment : "Good-
ness knows the trunk is big
enough. It's big enough for
two."

There is no mention if the Frank Thompson in the story is *the* Frank Thompson, the Canadian newspaper owner recently moved to Africa. Not long after Memorial Day 1967 Tony Bud was killed by three .38-caliber (mid-range wad-cutter slugs to be exact) in the face, at a range of about two feet, by a wrecker, a bar regular, who after being refused a twenty-dollar loan by Iggy was also refused by Tony, who couldn't very well compete with his only drawing card. With Tony gone I haven't been back much to the Chit-Chat.

Anyway, about a week ago, I went into the plumbing-supply house where I buy my materials and Frank, the counterman, asked for my home address and said that the boss wanted to mail me an invitation to the premiere showing of a new line of luxury plumbing fixtures, which the brochure said were designed to meet "the needs of the bathroom revolution of the seventies," no shit. By way of inducing me to go to a meeting of plumbers, all licensed except me (even Frank knows of my paranoia about Buildings-Department inspectors—about three years ago Mayor Lindsay proposed a bill that building inspectors be uniformed and Frank O'Connor, then president of the City Council and now a judge, objected vociferously, saying that it would be demeaning of the inspectors' positions—I dread the day when that argument is used about all cops), Frank said he would drive me up to the hotel on the Grand Concourse in the Bronx where the premiere was to be held, and that we could stop off at the bar where he hangs out up there, which, he explained, was run by a beatnik, too.

Frank is a good man with the typical affliction of plumbing-supply house countermen. Whenever there

are no customers in the store, Frank is supposed to cut
threads on both ends of a seemingly never-ending supply
of half-inch I.D. red brass pipe, all exactly fifty-eight and
five-eighths inches long. These are used by a politically
connected plumber to install showers above the bathtubs
in N.Y.C. housing projects which are deliberately built
with no showers so that this plumber can smash the tile
walls and install them after the tenants have moved in,
and then another politically connected contractor gets
the contract to re-tile. Frank's affliction is that the tips of
several of the fingers of his right hand look as though a
rat had gnawed at them as a result of losing small pieces
of flesh on the sharp cut threads faster than he can regrow
them.

The day of the premiere the beatnik of Frank's favorite
hangout turned out to be about forty-seven years old, the
unmarried son of the owner, and the possessor of the
most innocuous little goatee that I've ever seen, probably
grown to hide a weak chin. But if they didn't serve Jack
Daniel's, at least they had Jim Beam and plumbers rather
than house wreckers to drink with. After getting sufficiently juiced, I picked up Manuel, the only plumber I
know that I will work in the same building with, and we
made it over to the hotel and the premiere. No matter
what the Trots on the Lower East Side may tell you about
the revolution, as far as the American Standard Products
Company is concerned, the revolution of the seventies is
urinals that flush automatically as you step back from
them, and doctors' lavatories that both start and stop the
water running by proximity, this line being known as
"Hands-Off," no shit. Instead of mixer faucets with spouts

curved downward that have been in common usage since
Pompeii, the washbasins of the seventies will have an
opening pointing upward toward the user at a forty-five-
degree angle, something like looking down the throat of
a mortar. When the water is turned on, it arcs out in a
parabola ending in the center of the round bowl, and
looks something like those hideously obscene Belgian
statue fountains that were revived at Robert Moses'
World's Fair in 1964, which depicted prepubescent boys
pissing. Great for middle-aged matrons to get their rocks
off looking at, with no threat of real cock (D. H. Lawrence, I believe in a letter to Huxley's wife answering
her letter that she didn't want her teenage daughter to
read *Lady Chatterley,* explained to his friend's wife that
if a teenage couple went to a motion picture and were
so aroused that when they each got home, they mastur-
bated separately, then that motion picture was obscene,
but if after seeing the picture together they went to the
girl's house and made love on the couch, then that picture
was most emphatically not obscene).

There was only Scotch at the hotel in wax-paper cups
and little plastic cards with each plumber's own name
and firm name (mine had my name and the name of
the supply house where Frank works). Then we were
ushered into another room, where they went through
introductions of various regional managers and road men
for the manufacturer and torpid speeches. The highlight
of the premiere was to be a feature-length color movie
called, no shit, *Revolution—70.* It was prepared by a
Chicago-based p.r. firm, which should have known better.

After some really beautiful shots of natural waters

against various lightings shown behind the credits, the
picture itself was in that kind of brashly highlighted color
photography used in costume-jewelry ads in the *Sunday
Times Magazine* section. Three separate women are at an
art gallery looking at modernistic sculpture. Soon their
basic *venta* personalities emerge from the Chicago-chic
clothing and they start gossiping about beauty. It is an
obvious mental leap requiring no suspension of disbelief
to go from beauty to bathroom pottery. An overriding
stentorian *March of Time* voice starts, "Spectra 70—The
Everything Bath. Today 'taking a bath' has become an Art
rather than a mundane habit. It is a totally dimensional
experience that brings pleasure and relaxation to the
body, mind and spirit, and it is a private experience, free
from the day-to-day problems, large or small, that invade
our privacy. There is so little privacy left in our lives.
What there is, we guard. We close the door. We can revel
in the privacy of our bathrooms and truly, luxuriantly,
enjoy the pleasures of bathing.

"Today, too, the bathroom might even replace the
library in your home. A world of privacy for reading,
relaxing. It can be an ivory tower . . . a fully functioning
spa. It can be a palace in its own splendid and unique
way.

"Never before has the bath been so magnificently imagined and created. And everything is not only superb to
see, but everything works. . . . That's why we call it 'The
Everything Bath' . . . everything you can dream for your
private world of bathing and grooming pleasures. If these
wonders don't make you want to 'take a bath' instantly
(and over and over again) , nothing or nobody in this
world will."

Then, through a series of montage misty shots of beautiful slim chicks bathing (it must take enormous perverse imagination to make a ninety-minute movie, two-thirds of which is of naked women, and never show even a nipple much less a curly hair or sweet nooky) , various ecstatic female voices go on, "Spectra 70—The Everything Bath . . . not just a library, or a sitting room, or a relaxation spa, or a beauty salon. It is all of these things. Luxury unqualified in a setting to make your dreams come true, to realize your yearnings and fantasies at the close of the door. Doesn't it truly have everything?

"A water-control tower to turn your sensuous showering moments into an experience like you've never had before with an ordinary shower. An upper and lower stereo shower head, each designed to gently wrap and soothe every part of you. A hide-away spray for after-bath rinsing or hair washing. A quiet-fill spout to supply the new five-foot Spectra 70 bathing tub, a combination of fine sculpture and symmetry of design. A unique lumbar, slanted comfort back. The safety of its etched-in polka-dot Stan-Sure slip-resistant bottom surface. A safety assurance the Spectra 70 doesn't take for granted. And two safety bars on the Tri-Wall, where they should be for protection.

"Twin recessed ceiling lights illuminate everything, and you, too. The drop-down manicure shelf hides twin accessory shelves. Even a drop-down seat for foot grooming or washing or treating a child's scuffed knee. And exclusive Bone—the go-with-everything color shown here with two Ultra Lavatories—one for her, one for him—and the Compact/Vent-Away self ventilating toilet with the Margate Bidet. The Spectra 70 Group of products for the Everything Bath."

New voice, "I love the bath. There is one marvelously simple explanation for why I adore the bath so—and that, I believe, is because I'm a woman.

"You see, I really can't think of any other room where I can close the door and, in utter calm, engage in every one of my feminine fancies. Entertain my latest and wickedest fantasies. Endear my memories. Search down into my soul. Soar up to giddy heights of inspiration and profundity. And, at the same time, feel the most outrageously spoiled creature on earth.

"Here is where I can disrobe or robe in peace, examine my body (every single inch and pore, if I choose to), appraise it, admire it, or not, and decide and affect its fate.

"If a maharajah gifted me with an unfathomable fortune in jewels, it could not enduringly match the luxury of my pool. For in its steaming waters filled with fragrance and oils, I am warm and protected. I am soothed and refreshed. I am quiescent and dreamy. I am soft and glowing. I am relaxed and radiant. I am beautiful and desirable.

"I am wiggling my toes."

New voice, "How I love to do as the Romans do. But, oh—how fortunate I am to be living in this century and this country. For only now and here can I soak up both the grandeur of 300 A.D. and the brilliance of today.

"At this moment as I loll in my Roman pool, I can't help thinking that if Calpurnia had my Shower Tower with its upper and lower showers, and other delicious Ultra-Bath marvels—would Caesar not have spent the Ides of March with her?"

New voice, shot of Mies Van Der Rohe apartment

towers along the lake front and then of huge bathroom
with Modigliani print (poorly framed), "In my super-
charged city life my bath needs the luxury and sophistication that the French were famous for adoring. But it
has to be functional and can be surprisingly economical
by using my Ultra-Bath to serve two rooms. And so, I
love my unique but simple concept: Ultra-Bath duplex
with its folding doors that open up or close to make a
private bath or shower for me or my husband (as you
can see he likes a strong, contemporary look). Or I can
close my door and have my very own powder room. He,
too, can retreat into his own private, masculine world by
simply sliding a door on his side. Oh, how practical yet
provocative life can sometimes be."

New voice, Stanley Kubrick setting, "5, 4, 3, 2, 1—
Zoom! Up and away I soar through the heavens—to the
moon, perhaps. No, I believe I'm heading for Venus. I
must do my hair and put on my makeup now. I want to
look as beautiful as any woman on Venus. My husband
will prepare our landing shortly. But first he will work
out in the gymnasium. After all, it's not every day an
Earthman can come to Venus."

New voice, carved wood and false fascia-stone bathroom, "Every time I enter this beautiful room, it has the
power to calm me, and let me drift as lazily as I would
do on the sea. Notice (and you really can't miss it) how
the richness of Bone splendidly warms and adds another
dimension to my Mediterranean Sea."

On and on. In the auditorium at the faintest glimpse of
an upper chest swelling there were catcalls and whistles.
Manuel and I sat all the way at the rear, it was uncertain

if this was a self-exile. I was the only plumber there
without a necktie, having gotten dressed up for the occasion, I wore my Pendleton windowpane check wool shirt.
(When I was a junior in high school, I made the same
mistake. I escorted the daughter of Loft Candy to a hunt-
club ball. It was the only time in my life I have ever worn
a tuxedo—but it was white-tie and I was an obvious inter-
loper.) Nobody there who didn't know Manny could
figure out why he was wearing a piece. He always does,
being a P.R. and working on the Lower East Side, but
being a practical man, he carries not an ordinary snub-
nose .38, but a Smith and Wesson Chief's Special Model
#60, which is available in stainless steel. This is a model
marketed mostly in the South American tropics, where
its rustfree advantages greatly override the higher rate
of barrel wear in stainless. The perfect tool for a plumber
who doesn't want to get burned by slumlords not in the
habit of paying laborers. I have known Manny for several
years and have never seen him unholster his gun, but his
reputation is like that of the Berber tribesmen who
guard the U. S. Air Force SAC bases in North Africa. A
Berber may not draw his long curved knife and return it
without blooding the blade. If you ask a Berber guard,
as George Kazak, a former B-36 crew chief I once worked
with, did, to show you his knife, he will, but before
he returns it to its sheath, he will deliberately knick
the back of his own hand. You don't ask again. George,
who when I knew him was a shop manager and no longer
worked on machines, always carried a large, square-
shanked screwdriver stuck in his belt, even when he had
a suit on. He explained that aircraft mechanics always

carried a screwdriver when working out on a wing or tail surface or atop the fuselage. The greatest danger was of starting to slide and having no hand purchase. A sharp screwdriver served the same function as an alpinist's ice-axe in an emergency—being stabbed into the soft aluminum skin of the airplane, it could prevent a fifty-foot fall onto the concrete hangar floor. George liked emblems and would often tell about going into Casablanca, where there were French girls at the bars. On the bus into town he would place a small red anodized aluminum bolt and blue Ny-lok nut through the boutonniere hole in his left lapel. When he got into town, he would start up with the first available French girl who spoke English, telling her how unique he was, as exemplified by his name, which was Russian and spelt the same forward or back. When the girl got around to asking about his medals and particularly the one in his lapel, he would explain that that one was for screwing. If he was drunk enough by then, he would ask the girl if she had ever seen a one-eared elephant. When she said she hadn't, he would pull his left pants pocket inside out, unzip his fly and hang out his uncircumsized joint. He claimed that this usually worked, but I often doubted George's stories, as he claimed that French girls were so cheap that after they took a shit, they would take one sheet of toilet paper, pierce it in the center with the right hand middle finger, wipe their ass with the finger, and then withdraw the paper with the left hand, wiping the finger clean. All to save paper.

Joel Oppenheimer, the poet and namer of Max's Kansas City, divides all of mankind into two basic types—folders

and crumplers. Joel himself is an obvious folder, as am I.
(My former wife's orthodox maternal grandmother may
have been the world's most compulsive folder. Just before sundown every Friday night she would tear off and
fold neatly a stack of five-sheeted sections of toilet paper
sufficient to last her family until after sundown on Saturday. That way nobody had to violate the prohibition
against doing any work on the sabbath—apparently tear-
ing is work but wiping is next to godliness.) Joel is possibly the best occasional poet of our time, a skill that
derives from an ability to make clear distinctions. He had
pointed out this schism to me when I was planning to get
married some eleven years ago. I didn't listen to him and
the first revelation of my married life was that a fresh roll
of toilet paper was gone after one week. In the four years
I had lived alone prior to getting married I had used an
average of two rolls a year (which I stole from Rienzi's,
which had extras stacked on the bathroom windowsill)—
750 sheets per roll is 1,500 sheets over 365 days, or an
average of twice a day two sheets neatly folded each time
I shit. Such care is not to be confused with the Moroccans,
who use a single sheet to clear the finger, or the French
use of three sheets for two shits, as that entails hoarding
half-used paper. George never was very precise in his
stories. He gave up mechanics for a managerial position
and knew nothing of tool making.

Joel named Max's Kansas City for Max Finstein, another poet, who for the past eight years had lived in New
Mexico, where he went taking along Joel's first wife and
two sons. Diane Wakoski, by far the best woman writer

in the country and who goes into a rage if her name is
misspelt, defines poets as namers. For years she has been
making George Washington poems about her apocryphal
father George Washington. At times he only remains
apocryphal to her own mind, because he had no face hair
(if he had, he never would have suppressed the Whiskey
Rebellion). Besides George Washington, she also writes
about men with well-hung mustaches. She once mailed
me a lovely brochure of half-tone photos, *The Jack Daniel's Distillery No. 1, Lynchburg, Tenn., Established 1866,
The Oldest Registered Distillery in the U.S.* (almost as
long a title as an academic monograph). Daniel was
childless. So his sister Finetti's son Lem Motlow took over
when he died:

> Mr. Lem ran the distillery until he
> passed on in 1947. His influence was felt
> throughout every operation of the dis-
> tillery as he continued to make whiskey
> just as his Uncle Jack taught him. But he
> did change a few things, for it was Lem
> who persuaded Mr. Jack to change over
> from selling whiskey in the barrel to
> whiskey in the bottle. On the next page
> you'll see a flow chart, showing how Jack
> Daniel's whiskey was made in Mr. Jack's
> and Mr. Lem's time, and how it is still
> being made today.

Jack was only five foot two inches, wore a black frock
coat, wide-rimmed beaver and a fluffy silk bow tie. He was
balding and had a black pointed beard. He looked like a

stern entrepreneur. Lem was a big man with a paunch,
gap teeth, a bulbous drinker's nose, small bright eyes and
short thick fingers. He looked as if he would make a good
Santa Claus. Last month Diane sent two postcards:

> Am sitting in London's Heathrow Air-
> port waiting for my flight to Palma de
> Mallorca/Just overheard a man with
> Northern English accent at the next
> table saying/You can't get anywhere
> without a mustache/Does my mythology
> follow me/Or is it just my blue glasses
> that allow me to hear what I will/
> > love Wakoski

> You could make a fortune here as a
> plumber/You would like the mountains
> & this privacy (& the motorcyclists) here
> better than Vermont/Sorry I have to
> return to the States this week/
> > Wakoski

Her ears are pierced. She wants to marry the King of
Spain. I sometimes fantasize her in my mind when driving
on a moonlit night to Vermont. But she doesn't like the
smell of sour-mash bourbon on mustaches. She wants to
be the Janis Joplin of poetry. When she gives a reading,
she looks like a sexy Aimee Semple McPherson, but being
a poet, not an entertainer, she doesn't have Joplin's spon-
taneity (when Joplin was asked by a reporter at the
Woodstock Festival if there were boy groupies who followed girl singers, her immediate reply is supposed to
have been, "Not nearly enough").

JANIS NAUGHTY, FINED $200

Tampa, March 5 (AP)—
Rock singer Janis Joplin has
been fined $200 in Munici-
pal Court on charges of
using profanity during a
Tampa concert last year.

Louis Putney, attorney
for the 26-year-old-singer,
told Judge Nick Falsone
that Miss Joplin was on
tour outside the country.
Putney entered a plea of
no contest yesterday.

Miss Joplin allegedly
used obscene language
when detectives with bull-
horns interrupted her per-
formance to control the
teenage audience.

Diane once wrote a poem about a velvet and lace dress
that I had had custom-made for her as a present for Washington's birthday. A couple of years later she left it draped
over the back of my rocking chair when she flew out to
New Mexico and Arizona for a two-week reading tour of
Indian high schools. She's forever creating such situations
which signify too much to her—if I left it out for two
weeks to get wrinkled and dusty, I'd be unthinking, if I
hung it up in the closet, then that was because I didn't
want some other chick that I balled while she was gone to
see it ("Do you still beat your wife? &c.").

Before going into the Air Force and learning a trade,
George had worked in his father's silk-screen shop making

those pale blue signs with white lettering that diners use
to announce their daily blue-plate specials. He had ex-
panded the line by adding fillers like:

> When in trouble
> Fear or doubt,
> Run in circles,
> Scream and shout.

and:

> USE DISCRIMINATION
> when choosing where
> to spend your money!
> This Place Practices It!

When the movie ended, we were shifted to another
room, where there were display stands of the various com-
binations of new fixtures. One of the salesmen (there
were no bathing ladies in the flesh) explained how the
Luxor/Vent-Away self-ventilating commode had saved his
marriage. For $292.50 list price (plus installation), this
toilet automatically sucks away your farts even before you
flush it. He failed to say if it was he or his wife who was
flatulent. For $212.35 there was the Margate Bidet *sans*
fart-sucker. The Spectra 70 bathtub with tri-wall was
$397.75, plus $41.95 for recessed lights, and $352.75 for
stereo shower tower, all in exclusive Bone or Surf Green,
Manchu Yellow, Venetian Pink, Regency Blue, Fawn
Beige, or new Bayberry. Nobody there could tell me what
color bayberry was, it was too new. I failed to price the
Hide-away rinsing spray, the built-in Whirlpool and the

Ultra-Font trajectory lavatory faucet as I couldn't quite
see installing them in an artist's loft.

After the stand-up buffet of cold cuts, I split trying to
contrast the opulent masturbatory fantasies of the movie
with remembered snatches of Larry Eigner's beautiful
poem about a blind girl's fingered orgasm. Gil Sorrentino, one of the very few poets who is also an able critic
and even one who can admit to changing his opinion as
he did about William Burroughs, has on occasion used
the word "plumber" as a critical term of opprobrium in
describing a writer of piss-poor verse. Up until the premiere I held this against him. In older plumbing shops in
poor neighborhoods you can sometimes still find fly-
specked posters that show a clean journeyman plumber
with a quiet smile and the legend "Plumbers are the
guardians of the Nation's health." And it is true the 1919
Chicago typhoid-fever epidemic was spread by an inade-
quate plumbing code that allowed waste to syphon into
the fresh water supply under certain low-pressure conditions. Norman Mailer has described plumbing as "the pre-
vention of treachery in closed systems," and in the revo-
lutionary bathrooms of the seventies all those misty ladies
can prevent treachery in their closed systems while their
husbands get-off in the gymnasium. Lawrence's prescience
was wider-ranging than I had ever previously credited.

In the cab on the way to Max's after the premiere there
was another kind of treachery preventing closed system.
Almost all taxis in New York City now have jerry-built
aluminum extrusion and Plexiglas partitions that physically separate the driver and passengers and are supposed

to prevent or deter assaults on the driver, while offering none of the privacy that built-in limousine partitions used to. The cab partitions are built by the same companies in Queens that build aluminum combination screen and storm windows for landlords of rent-controlled buildings to obtain a fifty-cent-per-month per-window rent increase. These windows are fabricated in such a pinchbeck manner that they pay for themselves in two to three years and have a life expectancy of seven years. The cab partitions look to have a life expectancy of less than a year. About two years ago, in the listing of new patent grants in the *Times,* there was a notice that the Checker Co. (the only remaining manufacturer of five-seat vehicles specifically designed as taxis, most cabs in New York City today are bottom-of-the line four-door Fords which seat three with no leg or parcel room) had the rights to a full built-in partition that could be bolted from either the driver or the passenger compartment, offering each protection from the other's treachery. The article ended with a note that all orders from N.Y.C. had been for the driver's side lock only. By the same token, cab owners don't trust their drivers either. The older cabs use Argo meters, which are started and stopped by a large metal flag which indicates to anyone seeking a cab whether the meter is on or off. The newer cabs now have meters made in Sweden by Halda (the manufacturer of highly sophisticated time *vs.* distance gauges for use in sportscar rallies) which are actuated ten seconds after anyone sits on the seat (including the right and center front seats) so as to prevent the drivers from making flat-fee trips for themselves. Even the buses have changed. Bus drivers will no longer make

change (if you only have quarters and no dimes or
nickels, although the posted tariff is thirty cents, it costs
you fifty cents and the money dropped into the fare box
now drops directly down into a safe bolted to the floor.
The M.A.B.S.T.O.A. (Manhattan and Bronx Surface
Transit Operating Authority) claims this is to prevent
holdups, but it seems clear that it is basically an anti-
pilferage measure. Even the Avenue B and East Broadway
Coach Company has been coerced into following suit, but
their fare is only twenty-five cents. In my lack of street-
smarts I had always assumed that a social contract was
grounded on faith. But then again, when I was a little
kid, I thought sawn-off tree stumps were young trees, and
that horses gave milk because both the Bordens and Sheffields delivery vans in my neighborhood were drawn by
horses. The Sheffields driver had a better horse, she knew
which houses got deliveries and stopped only at those
accounts without the driver touching the reins. Hustling
cab drivers have discovered that if they press the manual
starting button on the Halda meters as you are opening
the door, before there is any pressure on the seat switches,
the meter will tick over an extra ten cents after ten seconds even if the cab hasn't yet started to move in dense
traffic. Hackies get fifty percent of the meter reading,
plus tips.

When I worked near the Delaware Water Gap ten
years ago, I rented a nice house for very little money because it was only a few hundred yards from the then new
atomic power plant at Turkey Ridge, Pennsylvania. The
contract for the plant was let to the lowest bidder, Scin-
tilla-Vertex of Switzerland (a large, diversified company

that among other things manufactures a superior solder-
ing gun and the world's finest racing car and aircraft mag-
netos) . Because the call for bids had not specified that
U. S. Standard threads be used throughout, the entire
plant was made up using Metric threads and wrench sizes.
Only after it was erected (by a Swiss crew) did anybody
stop to realize that American wrenches wouldn't fit (with
two exceptions—nine-sixteenth-inch and three-quarter-inch
wrenches are accidentally interchangeable with Metric
fourteen-millimeter and nineteen-millimeter sizes) .
Rather than buy Metric wrenches (the finest wrenches
made, both Metric and U.S., are manufactured in Milwaukee, Wisconsin, by the Snap-On Tool Corp.) , the
A.E.C. is allowing every nut and bolt in this power plant
to become stripped by the use of the wrong size wrenches.
I don't expect Halda meters to last too long, despite their
quality.

I started musing on when the N.Y.C. Housing Authority would start installing "Hands Off" fixtures in housing
projects. Public housing has had a strange history in New
York City. The first such subsidized apartments were not
built by the city at all, but by a rich man named Phipps,
who to his chagrin found that his black manservant was
not allowed to stay at the same hotel with him when he
visited the city. He built Phipps Houses on the corner of
Sixty-fourth Street and Eleventh Avenue (opposite the
Times printing plant) about sixty years ago. They now
qualify for the term "old-law tenement" (under N.Y.C.'s
archaic housing codes any multiple-occupancy building
put up between 1911 and 1919 is a new-law tenement and
any such building put up before 1911 is an old-law tene-

ment), but for their time they were far superior to anything then available to blacks. (About sixty years ago
N.Y.C. sponsored an architectural competition for the
design of what were to be called "model tenements." The
winning design first incorporated the hexagonal airshaft
between adjacent buildings, thus eliminating totally win-
dowless interior rooms in railroad flats. Fortunately
N.Y.C. has never had a window tax the way London and
Amsterdam did in the past. Fielding mentions that many
landlords would brick over the window openings in cheap
flats to evade the tax.) When I was a motorcycle mechanic
in a shop on that block, I had a chance to see them first-
hand. The city administration plans to tear them down
and put up an upper-middle-income Mitchell-Lama co-op.
Whenever such plans are anticipated (it always takes
several years to get everything lined up), the first thing
that happens is that the cops disappear from the block
and the garbage men only come around every third day
(the *Daily News* calls them "Sanit-men"). Not long after
that, the population of the block goes through radical
changes, and all those families with the slightest preten-
sions toward being middle-class are forced out by the
junkies, who are free from police constraint. When I was
last there, in 1966, Thelonious Monk still lived in Phipps
Houses. I was never in his apartment, but it was described
to me by several people I knew who lived in the same
building as a veritable fortress designed not so much for
living comfort as to exclude junkie burglars. I used to go
into Phipps Houses on the average of once a week to buy
back my boss's electric typewriter for twenty-five dollars.
Eventually the price went up to thirty-five dollars. My

boss's name was, no shit, Mr. Billig (in Yiddish *billig* is
the word for "cheap"). When the price of buying back
his own typewriter went up to more than the weekly cost
of a central-stations burglar-alarm system, he decided to
buy that service instead. The only times I would see
Monk was when he was in the street going to the grocery
store. Because he had at one time been unable to obtain a
cabaret card (necessary in N.Y.C. to perform in a place
where liquor is served, and summarily denied if you have
ever been arrested, not necessarily convicted), he was
something of a hero to Killer Joe (a gorilla, that is, a
man who grabs women from behind and then snatches
their purses after knocking the wind out of them) and
Peanuts (considered to be the smartest of the Sixty-fourth
Street junkies, so smart that once when stealing frozen
shrimp off a parked truck the driver returned unexpectedly and locked him in with the chain-mail rear gate from
which Peanuts had neglected to remove the padlock).
Despite this idolatry, Monk's apartment was not safe from
burglaries. I met Monk once. I was getting on the bus
coming down from Hyannis after spending a summer in
a shack right on the harbor in Wellfleet, which was being
dredged that summer, the stench making the shack un-
rentable to anybody of delicate sensibilities, but ideal for
a broke eighteen-year-old who had just quit college in the
middle of a term after having a lady dean in the English
department tell him that Geoffrey Chaucer was the
Robert Moses of the city of London of his day (even the
Times no longer feels compelled to print Moses' dreary
belletrist essays in the Sunday magazine section). As I
boarded the bus, there were no window seats left, so I

chose a seat next to a business-suited huge Negro. I was
reading John Clellen Holmes' novel *The Horn,* a murky,
adulatory fabrication about an alto-sax player who Holmes
seemed to think had something to do with Charlie
Parker. After a while the man next to me asked about the
book. I was young and full of my own kind of purist
adulation and kept putting the author down for not telling the truth about Bird. Finally through my own piss
and vinegar I recognized whom I was talking to (he had
told me he was a valet for some fat cat in Brooklyn
Heights) and started talking about Holmes' character
Junius Priest. There followed a two-hundred-mile double
put-on the likes of which I never expect to hear again,
between an ersatz valet and a boy jazz aficionado. I never
want to ever play the dozens with that man (the dozens
is not an exclusively black sport, not after hearing Joel
Oppenheimer cut Gil Sorrentino down asking Gil what
the greatest invention in the history of mankind was, and,
when Gil failed to answer, announcing "The wheelbar-
row, it taught the Sicilians to walk on their hind feet"),
but even so I'll never play the dozens with Monk. When
I was still in high school, if you wanted to hear Billie
Holiday or Monk, you had to go to a dismal nightclub
called The Cork and Bib in Hempstead, in Nassau
County. Cabaret cards are no longer required in N.Y.C.
ever since Frank Sinatra refused to be fingerprinted before he could get permission to sing.

Near where I live on Seventh Street is a group of ten
or so forty-year-old buildings called "First Houses," that
are, appropriately enough, the first municipally subsidized
housing in N.Y.C. They have all the cleanness of a Bau-

haus design, having been built as minimal housing for the poor. Two blocks away is a new twenty-two-story Mitchell-Lama co-op called Village View that's as functional and as lovely as the Pennsylvania State Penitentiary and not nearly as clever. If I ever had a Humanist conception, those two sets of structures would dispel such thoughts every time I pass them.

Riding in that cab trying not to think of revolutionary bathroom pottery and thinking about working in garages gave me a good chance to view my own circumlocutious thought processes. Among the older Austrian mechanics, and more particularly among tool makers, the worst possible term of opprobrium was to call a man a *schuster* (a shoemaker). It had always struck me as particularly just, since the name of the man who turned Willie "The Actor" Sutton in to the cops was Arnold Schuster. After robbing a bank, Sutton had gotten a job as a hospital orderly (probably the dreariest job imaginable) and gone unnoticed there for six months before Schuster spotted him on a bus and followed him. Sutton was arrested and Schuster collected his bounty money (if I remember correctly, it was ten thousand dollars). A day or two later (it is said that Vito Genovese saw Schuster on the television news and ordered the contract) Schuster was shot down in the street and killed; his killer or killers were never caught. Sutton had been (along with Legs Diamond) my childhood hero. Both were absolute loners, but where Diamond was the epitome of the insouciant two-gun killer, Sutton was the man who never hurt anybody, never even lived high, just a master of dissembling who had once tunneled his way out of the so-called unbreakable

Pennsylvania State Penitentiary. That's a difficult enough feat for one man to do from any prison by himself, but that particular prison is built like a spoked cartwheel, so that one guard seated at the hub of all the radiating spokelike cell blocks can watch every cell. Sutton broke out undetected, the only man ever to do it. He was turned in for bounty money and the informant killed by persons unknown, surely unknown to Sutton, too, who never was an organization man.

Crossing the 138th Street Bridge over the Harlem River, which separates the Bronx from Manhattan, the cab went through Harlem for a few blocks before entering East River Drive going downtown towards Max's. On the day in 1963 when the Post Office instituted zip-code numbers, several thousand people played 026 as that day's policy number (the last three digits of the Harlem zip code) —026 won. Policy numbers can't be fixed. The day's number is determined by the last three digits of the day's pari-mutuel totals. (When N.Y.C. first tried to make off-track betting legal, so as to increase its revenue base and to bring one more business under governmental control, Albany refused. But when Governor Rockefeller decided to institute a state lottery, the legislature approved it, but without the provision that the Chase Manhattan Bank, owned by Rockefeller's brother, have sole control over the operation of the lottery. The federal courts have since ruled that no bank can sell lottery tickets. The lottery pays back forty-six cents in prizes for each dollar spent in purchasing tickets—policy pays sixty cents on the dollar. After an initial flurry of interest, the lottery has failed to yield what was expected of it. Policy thrives.) The next

day an awful lot of policy banks failed to reopen. In the
days when Frank Costello ran N.Y.C., that sort of thing
never ever happened. Those were also the days when not
only an Arnold Schuster got his in the streets, but also
Vito Marcantonio (the last truly representative representative N.Y.C. is likely to see) could get gunned down on
the streets of Yorkville. On a Friday night there were
always men drinking in the bars on Eighty-sixth Street
between Lexington and First Avenues who claimed that
they saw a black Oldsmobile and Vito fall, but they
would never come forward except in those weird, hostile,
pay-days-only Eighty-sixth Street bars. There was one
blond-haired German with an accent that used to get
thicker the later it got (and not just from drinking)
until finally some Irishman would ask him where he
fought during W. W. II. Now, I've never met any
German who would answer that any other way than by
saying that he fought on the Eastern Front, except this one
who used to go into those bars every Friday night just to
get the shit kicked out of himself. And he earned it, not
so much by either his honesty (which I still question) or
the accident of where his number fit into the logistical
scheme, but because he was the worst kind of drinker—
the kind that expects the other drinkers in a bar to act
out his masochism for him. He was always back the next
Friday night to go through that compulsory ritual. At that
time I was working in a foreign-car shop on Eighty-third
Street and York Avenue, and I thought that those bars
were rough, but it wasn't until I moved to the Lower East
Side and Tony Bud started teaching me the kind of street-
smarts that a suburban upbringing had shielded me from,

that I began to learn what I hope I'll never need to know.
I'd walk into the Chit-Chat in the afternoon exhausted
and if no one else was in the place Tony would wait until
I'd slouch down on a stool and hook my heels on its rung,
then walk around to my side of the bar and ever so quietly
say into my ear, "If I pulled that stool out from under
you, you couldn't regain your feet in time. You're dead."
Or he'd ask me, "What would you do if a man came at
you right now with a knife?" I'd say that I'd break a beer
bottle. And he'd tell me, "OK—break that one there, right
now." The reusable bottles that bars get from the brewer-
ies don't break on the radiused mahogany edge of a bar.
Then he'd tell me always take a shell glass, the rim will
crack easily on the edge of a bar, and if push comes to
shove and it's turned against you, you can always crush
it in your hand before it gets pushed into your own
throat. Tony taught me a lot that I may never use, like if
you see a man walk behind a bar with his hat on, don't
let yourself stand between him and the front window,
because if a passing cop sees him, he'll assume it's someone holding the place up and you're in a direct line of
fire. There's a lot more that he taught or told me,
most of it less a matter of violence than that peculiar kind
of bar etiquette so necessary in poor neighborhoods (like
always put more money on the bar than you will spend,
that way a hustling bartender can't later claim you failed
to pay for a round, or that if a bartender empties a bottle
while pouring you a drink, he owes you a shot free),
but none of it helped him when a man he thought was his
friend put a police special in his face and blew it off.
Tony stopped smoking years before so as to keep his shirt

pocket empty, except for a plastic squeeze bottle, originally used to package nose drops, in which he carried
ordinary kitchen ammonia, it had always quelled close-
range trouble in the bar before.

When I walked in the door of Max's, Rus and Sam
were talking and the first thing I heard was Rus saying,
". . . no shit," and I was home. Sam was frantically wav-
ing an issue of *Field & Stream* magazine to show an ad
for a phosphorescent material that reputedly attracts fish
to your outboard engine's prop wash if pasted onto the
propeller blades. The ad was run by a firm called The
Berkeley Riot Toy Company, Inc., and their logo was a
spiked-ball and chain mace. The main difference between
Max's and any other bar (the reason that you so rarely
see a fight among the regulars there) is that, although
Max's is known as a painters' bar, it is in reality a writers'
bar, writers of sufficient subtlety to let the painters think
it's their bar. When the painters start talking, it's usually
about the new waitress (a subject known to interest the
writers also) or some mini-minded stripe painter (watching the angle formed by Pat's thighs—in a chrome-yellow
body stocking beneath her open-work crocheted black
micro-length dress—from hips to knees, the sophomoric
parochialism of these parallel-line painters becomes obvious) pontificating about art (e.g., Franz Kline's paintings are mere repetitions of Rouault's black outlining
without the color filler, an argument that always fails to
remember the 1966 Kline color show at Marboro-Ger-
stein, a show that had a yellow-centered painting with
more depth than any oil I've ever seen with the possible
exception of Erich Maria Remarque's Van Gogh gift to

the Metropolitan) , but these statements never carry any thought to a conclusion. At least in the days of the abstract-expressionists at the Cedars painters knew how to talk, like Wilhelmina, an action painter, who spoke so well about Artemisia Gentileschi, while puffing on her Mammy Yokum pipe, that she gave up painting and now is doing a lifetime book on that seventeenth-century lady painter, who apparently balled all the painters of her day and still produced a remarkable series of paintings of Judith and Holophernes, in which she, Artemisia, always appeared as Judith's maid. Willie may never finish or publish her book, but there are hundreds of copies of individual chapters circulating around like Joe Gould's notebooks. She no longer paints and has taken a job in the proofreading department of a Wall Street law firm so as to have unlimited access to a Xerox machine on which she makes copies of every interminable revision. She looks upon Artemisia's paintings of Judith as a harbinger of our increasingly rightist politics. I built a studio for Willie once in an abandoned saddlery shop that had been shuttered for fifteen years. The place was full of disintegrating harnesses, bridles, &c. and everything was covered with acrid flourlike brown leather dust which caused me to break out in a severe skin rash. Besides the money I made on the job, Willie sent me the following letter in recompense for my allergic reaction to the dust:

An Inventory of My Father's Camera Box

The box: A military surplus, WWI steel ammunition box, metal-stamped "AMM. BOX CAL. 50M2."
1 Camera—Retina IIA

1 Foldable camera tripod in case—secured in case by hand-
   knotted rawhide laces
1 Bertram Chrostar Light Meter
1 4"x3"x2" leather box with rawhide shoulder sling containing:
   assorted filters
   a lens brush
   a ten-second timing device in a tiny aluminum box—made
      in Germany
   1 camera screwdriver
   1 pair of tweezers
   1 watch strap gadget—function unknown
1 1½"x3"x2" leather box containing:
   2 pocket range finders—one of them rusted and corroded
   assortment of filters and lenses in little cardboard boxes
   assorted tripod hardware
1 stray Kodak filmspool
1 pocket slide viewer
1 hand timer release
a coil of extra rawhide lacing
1 pencil-size telescope distance finder (?)
1 Tynar F6.3 Anastigmat with an exposed film cartridge—a
   miniature camera ca. 1945
2 compasses:
   1—simple magnetic—U. S. Army surplus WWII
   1—prismatic Dry MK IX— (Canadian WWII—surplus?)
1 Camper's Watson's Matchbox—mfgd. in Fairfax, Virginia
   little aluminum container with flint striker attached to the
   bottom
1 folded sheet of sandpaper
1 1944 Diary-Calendar-Atlas
1 simple pencil compass
1 pair of Army-issue map dividers

1 collapsible aluminum drinking cup
1 sun clock—Johanson Mfg. Corp., Boonton, N. J.
2 pocket New Testaments: 2½"x3"
   1—flexible black leather covers, red-edged pages, inscription:
      "To Byron from his mother"
   1—flexible khaki covers—WWI—U. S. Infantry issue
Parts of my father's *inner* imaginative life not a part of the
camera box, but linked to it rather directly:
3 books and between them a *part* of the range of my father's
   imaginative life:
   Krazy Kat—George Harriman—standard picture-book edition
   produced during late 40s early 50s
   A standard, well-produced book of good photographs of the
   Mont St. Michel—same period
   A Serbo-Croatian grammar
re: My father's library: The Virginia Military Institute
     (VMI) has taken my father's fairly extensive *military
     library*—books on strategy, *Infantry Journal* publications
     and such as *The Politics of the Prussian Army* and *For-
     eign Maps*—editions, pubs. unknown.
     I have taken what I call my father's *folklore library* con-
     taining among other things the Everyman collection of
     the Arthurian legends in their different literary and his-
     torical versions. Significantly, everything *re* T. E. Law-
     rence.
     My mother has kept all of his Thomas Mann—a whole
     shelf—and most of his literature—also a few hard-cover
     representatives of his *Pocket Book* tastes. His Pocket Book
     library at one time containing practically everything pub-
     lished in it in the 40s and early 50s.
Biographical bits:
   He was born in Spokane, Wash. in 1897 and died in Roa-
noke, Va. in 1968. In the WWI he served in the French Ambu-

lance Corps and the 1st Div., U. S. Infantry. Throughout most
of his life he was a lawyer in the Veterans Administration in
Washington, D. C. and New York City. He retired from the
Government in 1953 because of Parkinson's disease. My mother
and he retired into Virginia and during the last years of his life
he was hospitalized in the Veterans Hospital in Roanoke, Virginia. The Australian novel *Ultima Thule* by Henry Handel
Richardson [*sic*] tells a story of the mental disintegration of
a very good (but perhaps essentially weak), romantic, sensi-
tive man, and the loyalty of the wife to the man caring for him
during the last years of his life. My father disintegrated *physically,* not mentally, but my mother's loyalty and care was
almost as much of a romantic fiction-come-true as huge areas
of my father's repressed imaginative life.

FINE

Willie's mind is akin to my own and she often makes
acute references. (E.g., Aberfan, a Welsh mining town
where after heavy rains the slag heap slid down and
buried the school, wiping out a generation. When relief
and compensation funds were contributed, the town ex-
piated its grief in public bickering over its distribution.)
She assumes if you can't follow her shorthand, you
haven't paid your dues. Anyway, with the minimal painters around now sounding like T. S. Eliot characters, it's
almost a relief after talking to one of them for ten minutes, if Jason Holliday (the queen of Shirley Clark's film
Jason) interrupts every conversation going at the bar at
once to recite,

> Fuck Easter,
> Shove it up your keister,
> I'll take a young kipper.

Rus started talking about reading Jim Lipton's book
An Exaltation of Larks, and not having realized that the
word "venereal," which Lipton uses in the subtitle of his
book on collective nouns, meant "of or pertaining to
hunting." At which Sam started to tell of the time that
Escoffier, Sir John Barbarole, Auden and Spencer were
sitting together at a café in Paris and a group of whores
walked by. Escoffier proclaimed, "A dozen of tarts," Sir
John, "A fanfare of strumpets," Auden, "A sonnet of dar-
lings," and Spencer, "An anthology of prose." (Lipton
tells the same story, but about four Oxford dons, and
disparages it as irreverent.)

Sam is the most truly devoted husband I know, but his
wife, Barbara, likes to worry a lot, it keeps her from getting fat. (One night when I was having dinner at their
apartment, Sam kept urging her to put on her new
stretch slacks until Barb got furious that he was inter-
rupting her dinner preparations and shouted, "What are
you, a pants freak?" Sam gets very crestfallen at such times
and answered, "No, I'm a Barbara freak.") Barbara used
to be a school volunteer (unpaid) until she got into a
conversation with two of the regular teachers about drugs,
Barb hoping to find a new connection. One of the teachers wanted to know if you could get a buzz from sniffing
white glue, the other said no but she should try Rexo-
graph fluid. Barbara also grew up in the suburbs. Every
year her mother would insist upon getting a new car not
out of greed, but because she used to drive the kids to
school and her husband to the train in her pajamas and
lived in fear of the car's breaking down. After they started
writing dirty books, Sam rented a brand-new Mercury

Montego to go up to Provincetown. It seems that in a
1969 Mercury it is impossible to direct the vanes of the
air conditioning so that it doesn't blow all of the ashes
out of the ashtray whenever you turn it on. So much for
new cars.

Sam no longer teaches classics. Whenever he wanted to
demonstrate to his students what a *fasces* was, he would
borrow a dime. When Johnson debased our coinage,
Gresham's Law immediately took effect and all the older
dimes disappeared. Sam feels that this had more to do
with a government that has gotten so large that it self-
consciously fears that it is becoming increasingly fascistic
and so had to take that emblem out of circulation. He is
now planning to go back to work on his doctorate. Barbara had a great-uncle who committed suicide upon getting his Ph.D. after a thirty-seven-year hiatus. She is afraid
that Sam may now leave her and the kids if he gets his
doctorate. Sam keeps seeking a school that will accept his
thesis. After Michael Ventris deciphered Linear B and
found all the known tablets to be fragments of warehouse
invoices plus some few laundry lists, a professor at Bran-
deis put forth what Sam feels is a specious deciphering of
Linear A. Sam claims that what it really reveals is the
beginnings of true medicine—that there is only one cause
of death—shit poisoning. Sam, like any poet, is always
trying to create order out of the absurdity he sees around
him. While looking for a school to accept his candidacy,
he is working on a monograph to be submitted to the
Philological Society. Its argument is that one of the rea-
sons that a foreign population in a city (whether by inva-
sion or immigration) so profoundly affects the matrix of

the native language is not just that they introduce their own words for new concepts and objects, but that the ever pragmatic merchants simplify their usage of the native language so that even someone less than fluent can read and comprehend their advertising. Once this void in the native language is created out of mercantile greed, it is filled by the outlanders' words, which carry the ring of fresh metaphor. His analyst says that he is just pencil-sharpening, but Sam lives on Delancey Street and ought to know.

Sam is a somewhat unorthodox teacher. His students often fail at first to grasp what he means when he tells them that there is an inevitable logic that a culture in decay produces the finest art. One in ascendancy is too busy with bricks. (In the Governor's Palace in Santa Fe, New Mexico, there is a display of how the early Spanish settlers taught the Indians how to make bricks. It goes on to claim that the Spanish introduced the concept of modular building blocks instead of mudded adobe. At Twana-saka, about ten miles south of San Ildefonso, where Maria makes her black pottery with a reducing fire and cow shit, is an unexcavated ruin that was abandoned by the Indians who settled first at Black Mesa and finally at San Ildefonso several hundred years before the first Spaniards came. The top of the remains of the kiva is still visible above the surface—clearly made of round bricks of adobe tessallated to form an interlocking pattern.) A culture in decay falsely claims to be busy with bricks. His best students learn without realizing what is happening, like the way you learn to whistle, or tie your shoelaces, or spell your own name. As he feels that his function is not so

much to impart specific knowledge as it is to teach ways
of approach to thought, he will often begin a term by
explaining how to determine the distance that lightning
is striking from you in a storm—when you see a flash of
lightning, start counting seconds ("one-thousand-one, one-
thousand-two, &c.") from the visible flash until you hear
the thunderclap. Since for all practical purposes you can
assume the speed of light is infinitely fast, and with the
foreknowledge that sound travels at approximately eleven
hundred feet per second, then for every five seconds
ticked off, the lightning struck one mile away. Sam will
start a lesson in Plato by citing that as long ago as the
fifth century B.C. Plato wrote about the overharvesting of
hillside timber being a primary cause of river silting and
consequent flooding.

Sam had just gotten back from California, where he
had attended a conference on ecology. As Pat walked by
laden with platters, Sam started jumping about, leafing
through his magazine until he came to a small display ad
at the back (in the section where kennels run ads for
hunting hounds and pointers) which he thrust at her.
There was an ad for a simplified version of her invention,
now called a "Sooper-Dooper-Pooper-Scooper." When I
got home that night, I found a postage-due letter from
Sam mailed in California:

> The best tool I ever found for cleaning
> an electric typewriter is a nine-inch
> beach feather (probably scoter). Hard to
> take a crap in the back country out here,
> rather it is hard to find something to
> wipe your arse with, cause everything

adapted to annual drought—arms war
started by evaporation protection devices
becomes self-escalating under browse
pressure—bigger and better thorns,
leathery leaf coats—in the East you can
always find something soft to wipe or
water to wash with.

No shit.

UPTOWN-UPTIGHT

ALTHOUGH I'VE LIVED in Pennsylvania, California, Michigan, New Mexico and a few other places around the country, I've always considered N.Y.C. to be my home (as much as a Jew, when push comes to shove, can call any one place his home). So much so that when I lost track of a girl (named Jenny) whom I've loved (as much as I can, in my own mind, use that concept—she and I each got married to other people—that was ten years ago), every year for the last ten years when the new Manhattan telephone directory came out in the fall, I have looked for her name and not found it. It never occurred to me that she might have moved to another city. Spring, several years ago, she called having seen my name in a *Village Voice* ad for a benefit poetry reading for LeRoi Jones (at the time when he was on trial in Newark). She had been living in Cambridge, Massachusetts, all that time that I thought she was maintaining an unlisted phone

number. An old friend of mine who for years was a disk
jockey on FM radio stations once blew a job opportunity
on an FM "cultural network" when at the interview the
personnel officer for the network suggested that he start at
their station in Cambridge, which he referred to as "the
cultural capital of the U. S." My friend, Bob, thought he
was joking and started to laugh, costing himself the job.
But Bob rarely held a radio job for long. The best one
he ever had he was fired from when he announced that
"Tums" (the sponsor) spelled backwards was "smut." He
is my age and claims to have heard Uncle Don's final
program (which I missed, but which my older brother
heard, although he didn't know what "bastard" meant).

Things heard on the radio, when I was young, had a
peculiar familiarity, and I accepted them as rote truth.
When I was eleven, I heard a documentary radio program
about syphilis. It was dramatized by several case histories,
the only one of which I remember now was about a
soldier and a divorced woman who met on a train and
stopped over for a few days in Chicago on their separate
ways to the Coast. After the program, I clearly remember
going across the hall to my older brother's room (I had
been sick in bed for about a week with a cold and a sore
throat) and asking him if maybe I had syphilis, as the
symptoms of early syphilis were the same as mine. He insisted that I did not and was not to ask the doctor about
it the next time I saw him. He became quite belligerent
about it and I felt that he was displaying the same kind
of ignorance about this new disease that the announcer
on the radio had said caused its unchecked spread. By the
next day I was allowed to go outside to the woods behind

the house and I forgot about being syphilitic. I recovered and don't have pointed teeth. But my brother says that since he and I both have eyebrows that grow together— we are sufficiently strange. I am sure that a nonsilver bullet can kill me. I believe my brother like I used to believe the radio before Martin Agronsky got canned for being a straight shooter. (He wasn't really fired, despite very calmly discussing the relative need, this in 1953 at the height of the McCarthy hysterics, to change the name of the Red Sox in order to protect the nation's security— he reappeared for two days in 1963 following Kennedy's assassination when the networks needed every man they could get—and he still had that beautiful whiskey voice.) Agronsky was to the radio what Leibling was to the newspapers, a ballsy critic of observed fact who could qualify his own work, and do it in good sound prose.

The bars in Cambridge are closed all day on Sundays and last call is at 1:00 A.M. on all other nights, so when I went up to Cambridge to see Jenny, we ended up taking the 11:00 P.M. shuttle flight back to N.Y.C. so as to be able to stay out and talk later. (N.Y.C. also has its own blue laws—bars must have last call at 4:00 A.M. and nobody may sit at the bar after 4:30 A.M., except Saturday nights, when the hour is moved up to 3:00 A.M., so that the people will be in better shape to go to church on Sundays. The bars cannot reopen until 1:00 P.M. on Sundays.)

Not having seen her for so many years, and Jenny not having been in N.Y.C. for as many years, we decided not to go to Max's, where there would be too many other people to talk to and so we went to the sand box (an

area uptown roughly bounded by First and Third Ave-
nues, east and west, and Seventy-third and Seventy-fourth
Streets, north and south, where most of the hard-drinking
uptown east-side bars are located; Tinker's at Second and
Seventy-fourth, Dr. Generosity's at Second and Seventy-
third, Allen's at Third and Seventy-third, Churchill's at
Third and Seventy-fourth, Soerabaja at Lexington and
Seventy-fourth, and sometimes Wilfred's at Second and
Eighty-eighth). Uptown east-side bars can be roughly
separated into two group, singles bars like Thursday's,
Friday's (the first of the singles bars, the name coming
from the fact that a "Gal Friday" could drink there free
on Wednesdays and Thursdays, just before payday—they
have a form on the inside of their matchbook cover that
pretty well sums up what singles bars are like:

> Met at Friday's
> Name................................
> Address...........................
> Phone#............................
> Yes☐ No☐ Maybe☐)

September's and Maxwell's Plum, and drinker's bars like
Tinker's. The drinker's bars tend to have a high percentage of speed (there called "angel dust") and down
freaks, and posers (like the group that each night come in
in their brass-buttoned blue blazers and conspicuously go
over the next day's entries in the *Morning Telegraph*).
Leibling claimed that the Colonel (up until his death several years ago the handicapper for the *Telegraph*) was one
of the best prose writers in America, and the only handicapper with a lifetime total on the positive side (if I

remember correctly, it was something like $2.41). Any-
way, they are bars where you can remain anonymous if
you wish and where they pour almost as well as downtown. The singles bars are something else again.

Their patrons (it seems impossible to call someone who
goes to them either a drinker or a regular) are young
executive types and office girls. Each night the young
executive types circulate among the tables where the
girls sit in pairs, every two or three minutes all the
men shift one table to the left and start rapping again as
fast as they can. The object is to see how many telephone
numbers you can collect in one evening. Very few on the
spot pickups are made, for that matter very few of the
telephone numbers are ever called. That is not the point
of the ritual, any more than that these bars exist to serve
liquor to drinkers. The idea seems to be not who can
get the most snatch or cock, but who can trade the most
put-downs and still smile. There are dozens of such smart
uptown bars where little drinking is done, and the management makes its money from the rapid turnover and
a minimum or cover charge. The women at singles bars
all have terrified eyes. They are all uptight and live in
high-rise apartment houses. When I still worked at the
motorcycle shop behind Lincoln Center, Jimmy, a huge
one-eyed spade who called me his "main-man" because I
once bailed him out of the Tombs on Christmas Eve,
where he was being held for excessive parking tickets
gotten driving the pickup truck for the owner of the
shop; Otto, an Austrian mechanic in his sixties, and I
would go out to the local combined pizza shop and bar
for lunch. Otto once described a time in Vienna when he

spent an hour in his underwear on a snow-covered fire
escape when the taxi driver husband of the woman he
was balling came home unexpectedly for a cup of coffee
mit Schlag (Otto was the type to remember) to warm
himself up. Jimmy, who was a classical Lemuel Pitkin
being dismembered by a system he couldn't grasp, talked
about a time he, too, got caught with his pants down, in
the apartment of a friend's wife in a N.Y.C. housing
project. His complaint was that, "They don't even give us
fire escapes." It was pointless to tell him that all high-rise
modern fireproof buildings, whether luxury or low-in-
come, no longer have fire escapes, but have masonry
interior staircases called fire towers. Jimmy was the
first person I ever heard use the term "uptight" and then
with its no longer primary meaning—"I'd like to get her
uptight," that is, both aroused and close.

But at least the sandbox bars tolerate long-hairs, and
if you happen to be with someone who likes mixed
drinks, you can get served. I once made the mistake of
taking a friend to the Chit-Chat who drank martinis
(since it had never occurred to me to keep vermouth in
the kitchen). This was after Tony was shot and the bartender (when she ordered a martini) just informed her
that "this is downtown lady," and she could get whiskey
with either Coke or water back, or beer by the bottle. His
conception and mine of what downtown means obviously
differ. His name was Stosh. Over half the Uky bartenders
on the Lower East Side are named Stosh. Polish bars tend
to be bigger and more convivial than Ukrainian bars,
but the bartenders are still named Stosh. The biggest bar
I've ever seen (it must measure over one hundred feet

long) is on St. Mark's Place at the former Polish old-age
home called The Dom, which is now a black discotheque
on the lower (barroom) floor and the Electric Circus
(Disneyland for spaced heads) on the upper floors. During W. W. II The Dom became a sailors' hangout.
On a busy night it would take ten bartenders to handle
all the sailors. It is almost impossible for an owner or
manager to keep track of his bartenders' stealing on a bar
that long. Most older bars have back-bar mirrors which
are there both as decor and so as to make the number of
bottles on the stepped shelves behind the bar appear to
be more impressive. At The Dom there are interspersed
among the back-bar mirrors several lights of one-way
mirror, and behind that there is a catwalk so that the
manager can keep an eye on the bartenders unobserved.
It is similar to the way all U. S. Post Offices are built to
this day. Every Post Office has an exterior door (to which
nobody, not even the postmaster of that office, has a
key) which leads to an elevated, concealed catwalk that
circles the entire floor. Every few feet there are slits,
much like medieval balistraria, through which a traveling
Inspector General can spy on all the employees. Bartenders are traditionally paid very little as it is assumed that
they all steal, in one way or another. Downtown bartenders tend to overpour for their regulars, so that they
make their money in the cup. Bosses prefer this to just
outright not ringing up drinks and pocketing the money,
since it keeps the customers coming back. It seems more
honest to me to make money by giving away the boss'
booze than taking his cash, but one way or another a
younger bartender figures to make $250 a week, generally
with a base pay of $20–25 a shift.

Both the singles bars between Fifty-ninth and Seventy-
second Streets, and the drinker's bars from there up to
Eighty-eighth Street, tend to be bust-out bars (that is, a
bar that tries to make as much money as possible in the
shortest possible time, rather than build up a steady
trade). Even Dr. G's, the best of the sandbox bars, sells
two-dollar tickets at the door on weekend nights good for
two speed-rack drinks (house brands). A good bar will
just exclude tourists on weekends (so as to leave room
at the bar for regulars), not try to get rich off them. Dr.
G's is redeemed by the fact that they have a printing press
in the basement where they print poetry broadsides that
they give away, and a few times a year have poetry readings by poets who are drinkers (like Paul Blackburn),
although I have never seen a poet of his own choice drink
north of Twenty-third Street. In addition to poetry they
also print occasional posters, e.g.,

ATTENTION ! !

in the public interest
Doctor Generosity
Will Freely Demonstrate
Live, For Your Amazement
"SALOON ETIQUETTE"

(As recognized by international social whirls)
featuring such long neglected topics as:

SEE BELOW

"stylized wrist to lip action"
"securing & maintaining a dry elbow position"
"appreciation of innumerable visual effects"
"drink pacing"

"controlling over-indulgence"
"pros & cons of astrological come-ons"
"how to avoid occupational come-ons and
their emotional comedowns"
"peripheral vision in relation to appreciation of
more than one member of the opposite sex"
"acclimation to an unusually comfortable environment"
"food *can* be an outstanding saloon pleasure"
"strategic areas advantageous for maximum
front view & profile exposure and how to fully
utilize them"
"eye dialogue and its significance: with & without
back-bar mirror"
"utilizing the trip to and from the rest rooms to its fullest"

ALL URGED TO PARTICIPATE AND BENEFIT
NOMINAL FEES

Advanced Habitués Take Notice
Times Are Rapidly Changing
Overconfidence Is a Social Cancer
Try Our Refresher Course Before It's Too Late!
Even Your Best Friends Won't Tell You!
Start Now! Study 7 Days a Week with Experts & Reformed
Amateurs
from All Walks of Life
Strengthen Your "Spiritual" Character and Social Bearing
Forever
Doctor Generosity's Institute Of "Higher" Achievement
73rd St. & 2nd Ave.

David McSheehy, the proprietor of Dr. G's, looks like
Frank James and the place is papered with reproductions
of old James brothers bounty posters. It is one of the few

bars that still sells beer by the pitcher, $3.50. But the bar-
tenders don't mop your change, which can't be said of all
uptown bars. Tony of the Chit-Chat once told me that
the reason he always wore elastic braces was so that if
he was trussed-up after a stickup, he at least wouldn't be
tied with his own belt. Uptown many of the bartenders
affect suspenders with no such rationale. But then there
is no real tradition for middle-class bars. Where I grew
up, in a suburb of N.Y.C., there were two cocktail
lounges, which was where you went with somebody else's
wife, and three or four whore bars clustered around the
Merchant Marine Academy, where the cadets drank and
got laid—carefully tolerated by the town so as to protect
the local high-school girls. I still remember hearing an
ad on WJZ (now WABC) when I was fifteen or sixteen
for National Tavern Month. The copy was about going
to your neighborhood tavern for friendship and relaxation. I knew from my own limited observation that this
was not true (at least of my neighborhood), but I also
knew the radio wouldn't lie. That sixty-second spot, paid
for by the F. & M. Schaefer Brewing Co., has totally
altered my life. On my eighteenth birthday I took the
LIRR to N.Y.C. and headed for Cedar Street (three
blocks below Cortlandt Street, almost at the tip of Manhattan) to find the Cedar Street Tavern (which, of
course, was then located at Eighth Street and University
Place). Cedar Street at that time (before the World
Trade Center) was in the center of a mercantile section
and at night only had one street light per block. I finally
gave up looking and walked north on Broadway almost
convinced that the friendship and ease of a tavern were a

myth after all. When I got to the Village, I found a
telephone booth and looked up the address and had my
faith in the radio.and bars restored. The only tradition
the middle class has of bars is the disclaimer that the only
reason the workingman drinks in bars (rather than in
the comfort of his own home) is that he can't afford to
lay out the money for a whole bottle of whiskey at one
time—an argument as specious and dismal as Malthus'
and yet still being put forward by the Sociology Department at N.Y.U. as late as 1959. But then that was the
same year and college where I took a Henry James course
taught by the noted scholar Leon Edel. In explaining
that the proper pronunciation of the second vowel in
the name of the character Maria in *The Ambassadors*
was "I," not "E," as in "Black Maria," he gave an un-
matched etymology. He said that there had been an
enormously fat Negro whore working the waterfront bars
in nineteenth-century Boston. When a drunken sailor
got too unruly and the police had to be called, the whore,
whose name was Maria, would sit on the captive until
the police arrived to haul him away. All of which sounds
good, except that Partridge cites its first appearance in
print in *The Seven Curses of London* by J. Greenwood
(London, 1869) ; "The van that conveys prisoners to
gaol—Black Maria," and goes on, "By personification: the
van is black and *Maria* was perhaps suggested by the
letters V.R. (Victoria Regina) painted on its sides; the
ria of 'Victoria' may have evoked *Maria,* of which *Ria*
is a Cockney shortening." Scholar *vs.* poet—Charles
Olson made *Maximus From Dogtown* from the drunken
sailor John (or possibly Andrew) Merry confronting a

great bulk at night, Leon Edel made a specious etymology. Until this generation most Jews didn't drink in
public (the town I grew up in was sixty percent Jewish)
—although I can't place a pioneer Jewish drinker the way
Chagall can be said to be the first to have broken the prohibition against graven images. There is really no com-
pendium of data on drinking as a reflection of life. I once
watched every late-night TV movie for six months and
found only two (one with Frank Sinatra, the other
Humphrey Bogart) that treated bars as anything other
than a defeatist place of last resort.

The other extreme from Generosity's is Thursday's,
with its polished brass bartop and slink covered bar
stools, where the bartenders all wear gold foulard vests.
As the ma & pa neighborhood workingman's bars and
the hat bars peopled by heavies, off-duty cops and junior
Maf soldiers are forced out by the new high-rise buildings and their uptight tenants, more and more bust-out
bars will appear. I think my five-year-old nephew in
Washington, D. C. will reform all this. He came home
from kindergarten last week and sang for his mother (to
the tune of "Frère Jacques") :

> Marijuana, marijuana.
> LSD, LSD.
> Scientists make it.
> Teachers take it.
> Why can't we?
> Why can't we?

The liquor business is the most tightly controlled in
the state. In addition to the S.L.A. and the A.B.C. the

I.R.S. has a hand in also. Now every bartender pours
down bottles so as not to start the evening rush with
nearly empty bottles, but if the I.R.S. becomes suspicious
that the bartenders are hashing the booze (pouring a
cheap brand into a bottle with a more expensive label)
rather than marrying it (pouring down into the same
brand so as to consolidate several partially used bottles),
they will send in a team of inspectors with a spectrom-
eter to test every open bottle in the place. If even one
bottle is hashed, they will fine the owner twenty-five
dollars for every open bottle behind the bar. In a two
or three station bar this can easily amount to five thousand dollars. The fine must be paid before the bar can
reopen its doors. Judge Roy Hoefines, who owns the
Houston Astro-Dome as well as large range holdings in
Harris County (the largest beef-producing county in
Texas), drinks Jack Daniel's mixed with Diet-Pepsi according to *The New York Times.* With that kind of
drinker hashed bottles can get by. But then Houston is
the city where two or three years back a local George
Metesky bombed a children's playground, causing extensive injuries and deaths. It came out later that the am-
bulance drivers were picking up the bodies of the dead
children first (while there were still bleeding children
lying on the ground) so as to be able to make kick-back
deals with the undertakers. Possibly the most stringently
enforced of the S.L.A. statutes is the one requiring that all
places that serve booze be called a "bar and grill" and
never a "saloon." My father says he remembers when he
was young many bars that managed to comply with the
law by having one slice of bread and one slice of Ameri-

can cheese sitting on a saucer in the center of each table.
It was changed once a week, but it complied with the
law. Tinker's, which has a kitchen of sorts, has been having S.L.A. troubles for years because Tinker tried to put
out a sign using the word "saloon." The other unchange-
able law is that a bar may not be opened within two
hundred feet of a church. McSorley's Ale House is
located on Seventh Street between Second and Third
Avenues opposite the Ukrainian Orthodox Church and
for years now the church has been trying to have Mc-
Sorley's door shut, but they haven't succeeded, because
the church was erected years after McSorley's (which is
still owned by the original family) opened for business.
Although bascially an Irish workingman's bar McSorley's
has long had a percentage of the writers' and artists' trade,
unaccountably the two groups fitting well together there.
In the last few years college kids from Cooper Union
around the corner and from Washington Square
College of N.Y.U. a few blocks away have been using it
for a hangout. They are generally the less interesting
students, being reactionary and anti-drugs and drink only
as a peer-group social protest. The men on the stick there
have reached a compromise that is never spoken about
—they charge the kids a higher price than the drinkers
right next to them, and just don't serve them at all on
Friday nights when the Irishmen come in with their pay-
checks. Paul Blackburn lives on Seventh Street just to be
near McSorley's, and he and Bob Bowles, the painter,
have for years been altering the street sign of the one
block long north-south street that runs from Seventh to
Sixth Streets parallel to the Bowery but one hundred feet

further east. Up until about a month ago I had always
thought the name of this bastard one block long street
was Ale Place. I was talking to Paul one night and mentioned Ale Place and he told me the story. The proper
name should be "Hall Place," but every time the Department of Highways puts up a new sign they take it down,
paint out the "H" and alter the final "L" into an "E."
McSorley's ale is so well known that Rheingold puts it
up in both bottles and kegs for them and it is sold
throughout N.Y.C., but I gave N.Y.C. too much credit in
naming a street after it. Most S.L.A. regulations have
some grounding in the Puritan ethic, but some seem to
be there as a reminder to drinkers that the existence of
government is its own justification (e.g., Jack Daniel's is
made in two grades—black label, which is aged eight years,
and green label, which is aged six years and sells for a
dollar a bottle less—considering the quality of some of
the panther's piss that can be and is legally sold in New
York State, there seems to be no rationale for the fact
that green label is not listed in the S.L.A. handbook and
so cannot be legally sold here). As soon as you put an
ice cube in a glass of green label it is impossible to tell it
apart from the eight-year-old Daniel's—it is certainly every
bit as good as Ezra Brooks or George Dickel or any other
premium-grade sour-mash bourbon.

There are all sorts of gimmicky bars uptown like
Malachy's II, where Anny (a girl with the most beautiful
eyes I have ever seen) works as a barmaid. Any bar that
employs barmaids gets very few chicks drinking at them.
(Compare the occupational disease of Playboy bunnies,
who all have cigarette burns on the outer side of their

thighs, just where their bikinis end, from jealous wives
sitting with the fat businessmen who go there—always
accidentally inflicted, of course.) The customers of necessity are not regulars as they soon realize that there is
no chance of scoring. Such bars are generally located
where they can get office workers and tourists for a lunch
trade.

The regulars uptown for the most part constitute a
microcosm of capitalism. A bartender on his night off will
go into up to a dozen other bars, buy one or two drinks
and leave a ten-dollar bill at each place. Most of the regulars are other bartenders or bar managers, they tip anywhere from a hundred to five hundred percent, and expect
the others to spend likewise in their bars. It creates a
falsely inflated cup, but very little rent money. The more
literate uptown bartenders refer to this as "the floating
fund." Downtown a fair cup is twenty-five-dollars a night
and a fifty-dollar night is memorable. Day and night bartenders operate differently. A day man will generally use
a rocks glass for a cup and, if he receives a dollar bill,
will fold it up so tight that from across the bar it appears
to be no bigger than a quarter (a rocks glass will hold
thirty dollars in quarters) . Night men usually use a glass-
bottomed pewter tankard (being too rushed to fold up
bills) so that the boss can't see what's in it (the one
thing that an owner or manager can never, under any
circumstances, even touch is the bartender's cup.) It
seems only appropriate that glass-bottomed tankards be
used for bar money. Originally they were developed by
tavern keepers in England during the eighteenth century
to protect their customers from army recruiting officers.

It had been common practice for a soldier to come into
a tavern and start drinking with several men. After he
got them sufficiently drunk on beer, he would slip a coin
into each of their metal or crockery mugs. When they
drank down to the coin they were deemed to have accepted the King's gold and were impressed into the army.
The glass bottoms allowed a drinker to peer into the
bottom, beneath the head on the beer, and check for a
coin before drinking.

The middle ground between the uptown and downtown bars (of course, there are also a great many places
where you have to wear a suit and tie to get in—but they
can't really be termed bars) on the east side are places
like Connelly's on Twenty-third Street, which is not a
hat bar, but is the stand-up bar (a place where a cop
pays his way, by choice it is often out of his precinct, like
any other customer, where he is upstanding, not drinking
or eating free sitting in the back room) for a lot of cops.
They are Irish bars that pour better than places like the
White Rose chain, which has daily specials for forty-five
cents and fifty-five cents in three-quarter-ounce shot glasses,
and no buy-backs (free drinks) and yet never became
more than neighborhood bars. They carry brands like
Carstairs that are not even stocked by most bars. By pure
chance Joe and Gil Henderson and I went into Connelly's
one year on the night the Miss America awards were being given out. We were all a little juiced and decided to
stop off for a shot before we got to Max's from a gallery
opening on Fifty-ninth Street of Gil's sculpture. The announcement for the show had had printed in the lower
left-hand corner "No dogs/No dealers," but as the ad had

appeared in the *Times,* it had read, "No dogs/Principals
only," Gil was furious and wanted to bomb the *Times*
that night. The Miss America awards were being sponsored by Clairol; their ads at that time consisted of a
string of statuesque pretty ladies stating what their hair
color was. The last one stood up in her resplendent gown
and announced, "I have a rich, warm brown." Joe and
Gil both became hysterical and none of the Irishmen
could understand why, but it saved the Times Tower for
Allied Chemical that night. A confused old Irish bachelor
started muttering about how beautiful they all were, and
how he came to Connelly's every year to watch the Miss
America Pageant, and trailed off about what ever happened to Miss Rheingold (what happened to Miss Rheingold is that one year they put in a black entry to appease
what they were beginning to suspect was a substantial
part of their market) . We all decided to leave while we
were ahead and went to Park and Seventh, where the
drinks are larger and the beauties more palpable.

Anyway, Jenny looked just as good as she had when
she had been eighteen, but I figured she had been such a
marvelous fantasy all those years it couldn't help but be
disappointing if we took up again ten years later. There
is a girl named Ahza (her mother was a Magyar gypsy
who had read Pushkin)—the first waitress Mickey, the
owner of Max's, ever hired who wore glasses. The first
time I saw her I figured she had to be a bitch in bed to
carry off those steel-rimmed glasses above Mongol cheek-
bones (only a Cherokee can rival a Hungarian for facial
bones) . I have never even spoken to Ahza, having the
same sense about her and my fantasies as I do about

Jenny. The one thing I will always value most about
Diane is that she taught me that my inventions were always more interesting and gratifying than the truth.
Jenny had always been very domestic and was now trying
to market really very well made and beautiful crocheted
mini- and maxi-skirts. I spent two days at it and lined
up seven boutiques that were interested. She is now back
in Cambridge doing her crocheting, living with all that
culture, and I am back at Max's remembering the first
girlfriend I had, when I was thirteen; her name was Carol
Robertson and her father taught at Princeton. He used
to take her on fishing trips, and the first machine I ever
built was a worm snare that I made for Carol. It consisted
of a flat-box that petunias had come in that spring, with
the bottom slats removed and replaced with hardware
cloth (galvanized wire screening with half-inch square
openings) and filled with a loose mixture of humus, peat-
moss, and week-old iceberg lettuce. To use it, you hosed
down the soil for several square yards and placed the trap
on top of the mud. The next morning you took the flat-
box and shook it hard. The soil would sieve out, leaving
a couple of dozen fat earth-worms which had been gorg-
ing on the lettuce, and made the best possible early-season
trout bait. Max's is a bar where you can think such
thoughts and get neither yourself nor the bartender uptight.

OUTLAWS

Diane called from Max's and said she would buy me dinner if I would bring along a basic book on ferrometallurgy and lend it to her. When I got there she explained that her latest lover was a welding sculptor who insisted that he would only get married if he could get the daughter of Bethlehem Steel as a wife—so as to have unlimited access to a steel-fabricating mill. Diane, who has just enough knowledge about most subjects to know her ignorance, usually writes poems with one prevailing metaphor that she embroiders around. She needed additional specific knowledge and vocabulary about the conversion of iron into steel for a love poem to her sculptor, using as a metaphor her open-hearth furnace. She is a most unsubtle woman when it comes to her desires and is fascinated by the processes of mechanics. I tried to explain to her that neither Bessemer nor open-hearth converters were considered to be as good as the newer electric

furnaces which didn't introduce gaseous impurities as
the older processes did—but that wouldn't fit her poem
and she would hear nothing of it.

She has only recently started drinking, and so tends to
experiment with many different drinks, and like most
people who don't really like the taste of alcohol, she often
has mixed drinks. Today she was drinking rum and Coke.
My older brother Eric, who is an organizer for the Parade
Committee and works on Seventeenth Street a block and
a half away from Max's, came in and joined us. He
started telling Diane that if she was going to drink rum,
she should drink Lemon Hart. She liked the name and
ordered another round. Lemon Hart is 151 proof and
quite potent. Lemon Hart & Sons, Ltd., have been suppliers of grog to the Admiralty since 1804. Eric doesn't
drink much but he knows a lot about booze—like the
tequila in the mountainous parts of Mexico gets its yellow
color from dissolved silkworms. Diane wanted to know
why "proof" was used rather than percentage to denote
alcoholic content. All I could think of was that the term
proof was used in determining the bursting strength
of guns, but that didn't help. Eric explained that the
old test of a whiskey had been to pour out some black
gunpowder and then wet it down with the whiskey to
be tested. If it could be ignited with a spark it meant
the whiskey was at least half alcohol. Thus booze that
proved to be acceptable (100 proof) was fifty-percent
alcohol.

Diane is much like Eric and me in that she collects,
remembers, and uses isolated esoteric facts to clarify her
life (and, in her case, her poems) . She once wrote a poem

called "Cerise" contrasting her then husband's contemporary values with her enduring need for Beethoven. It
ranges through all the possible uses and misuses of the
color and fails to note that its most notable use in N.Y.C.
is that it is sprayed on the edges of unsold newspaper
bundles returned for credit to the publishers by news-
stands. She didn't like that fact (that poem and marriage
having long since been completed), so I tried another. In
1927, seven years after Prohibition had gone into effect,
Iron Trade Review (an industry trade paper) reported
that Americans were buying domestically manufactured
corkscrews at the rate of 25,000,000 annually. I want to
see if that comes out in her ironmonger poem.

Diane left to write her poem, and Eric headed downtown toward the fabric houses which line the side streets
between Houston and Canal to look for cardboard tubes.
Despite the efforts of our economy to make all packaging
non-reusable, painters and pacifists are going to subvert
the system. Painters use the cardboard tubes that carpet-
ing comes rolled around, generally six to eight inches in
diameter, to roll up their unstretched canvases without
cracking the paint. The N.Y.C. Police Department forbids
the use of wood or metal poles as standards for banners
and flags at any demonstration that they don't like, fear-
ing that they might be used as Kendo staffs (*bokken*)
against them. So the pacifists collect and use the two-inch
diameter cardboard tubes that were originally used as
cores for rolls of light fabrics as standards. (I've never
seen a parochial school marching band forced to use a
paper tube, with or without *flugel,* to carry their flags
and banners.) Even when American industries try to

sound like environmental conservationists, they come off
as absurd as Sam driving to an ecological conference in
Washington, D. C., in his smoke-spewing Saab. Two recent
ads: Reynolds Aluminum on the full page inside front
cover of a recent issue of *Natural History* suggests, "There
are two national problems which we believe no materials
producer should ignore: litter and conservation," and
goes on to propose a system of "mining" of thrown-away
all-aluminum beverage cans. It suggests that Boy Scouts
can earn up to two hundred dollars per ton on such
salvaged cans for fund-raising drives. The ad is illustrated
with an aerial photograph of an aluminum scrap-reclama-
tion plant built in 1969, in which a quarter of the factory
is obscured by dense smoke pouring from its stacks. The
other, an ad in the October 1969 issue of *Institutions
Magazine* (a trade paper of the hotel and restaurant business) run by the Glass Container Manufacturers Institute,
Inc., headed, "How to make more money by spending
less and doing next to nothing." It cites survey figures
to the effect that the retailer can make from ten to seventy
cents more per case on throw-away bottles, and that eight
out of ten customers prefer soft drinks in bottles.

Sam came in, just back from a conservationists' convention in Washington, with a roll of blueprints under
his arm. I told him of the Reynolds ad and we started
talking about ways to prevent any further mucking about
with the environment. Sam, being a much more pragmatic man than me (I was thinking in terms of governmental ownership of utilities and more efficient
machines), suggested that all broad-base taxes be abol-
ished, that income taxes should be retained only on a

graduated scale for the rich and that a major new tax be imposed on the consumption of horsepower and resources and on the production of unconsumed products (wastes), that is, tax all that is wastrel. What constitutes a waste product is relative to the degree of sophistication of the system. Ethylene glycol is a by-product of the production of cured vulcanized rubber that for many years polluted the Cuyahoga River in Akron, Ohio. Until somebody realized that since the river didn't freeze in winter for miles below the rubber factories, then ethylene glycol might be used as an automotive anti-freeze (in fact, it is far superior to the then used alcohol, due to its higher boiling point) and a profit was to be made rather than a river be polluted.

While in Washington, Sam had gone to the Navy Department and picked me up copies of the hull and rigging plans for *The Flying Cloud* and *The Great Republic*. He had also gotten a reprint of Lt. M. F. Maury's 1851 whale chart for his twelve-year-old son, Ezra, who is assiduously reading *Moby Dick*. *The Flying Cloud* was a three-masted clipper (the fastest ever to sail) built in 1851 that twice made the trip from N.Y.C. to San Francisco in a record eighty-nine days. She was 209½ feet long and just under 41 feet wide at the Plimsoll line. *The Great Republic* was a four-masted clipper launched three years later (the largest ever built) that measured 325 feet long by 53 feet at the beam. She burned to the water before she was fully fitted out. Even with copies of Mackey's original drawings, Sam and I will never settle our years-old argument about whether *The Great Republic* could have beaten *The Flying Cloud*. Obviously

the larger ship would have been a more efficient bulk-
cargo handler and therefore should have made her under-
writers more money, but steam was already encroaching
and speed could command a premium price both ways
from Sutter's Mill. While in Washington, Sam had talked
to the paleontology curator at the Smithsonian about an
article that had recently appeared in *Scientific American*
that claimed that the foreleg sockets of the American
Jurassic brontosaur, which have before this always been
reconstructed to face outwards (that is, opening towards
the sides of the animal), actually faced forward. If this
were true then the brontosaur would have been a fast
runner and more suited to the plains than the swamps
that he is now associated with. If this is so, then it may
be that their remains have only been found in swamps
because that is where a few strayed and were trapped and
preserved. To Sam this means that the United States may
be grossly overestimating its hydrocarbon fossil-fuel re-
serves, to museum curators it means re-numbering a lot
of bones.

There are a great many straight customers who eat at
Max's (it is among the top ten restaurants in N.Y.C. in
gross sales) and indirectly subsidize the bar regulars'
drinking habits. A couple in their sixties sitting in the
booth behind us had heard Sam and me talking about
clipper ships and asked us to come over and join them.
This seemed so unusual that we did. Their names were
Tom and Mary Stephens, and they told us for openers
that Tom had been President Eisenhower's appointment
secretary, but as they seemed to enjoy drinking, we sat
down. Tom started talking about being out in Colorado

with Eisenhower on a short official (golfing) visit when the
President had his first heart attack and their stay was ex-
tended, and meeting an old prospector named Orlo Ray-
mond, who worked Black Creek outside of Culver City.
He lived in a cave in the side of an earthen cliff and got
out enough gold so as not to have to work for anybody
else. He had a small sluice, about twenty feet long, that
was lined on the bottom and sides with ordinary carpet-
ing that he had picked up in the town dump. He would
spend the morning drawing bottom sand and gravel up
to the head of the sluice with his mule, then open the
gate and let the water wash it out again. Then he would
remove the carpet and wash it out in a big galvanized
tub. He then boiled the wash water down until there was
only a tumblerful left along with black dust with occasional glinting specks that had washed out of the carpet-
ing. He would then add mercury to this muddy mixture
and stir it thoroughly, letting the mercury form an amalgam with the gold—just as a dentist does in making gold
fillings. This would sink to the bottom of the glass and
he could then rinse away the worthless mud. He would
place the amalgam in cheesecloth and squeeze it as he
heated it. This would allow the mercury to seep out
through the porous cloth and leave him with fairly pure
gold. In a week he could gather an ounce which he
could then sell in town for thirty-five dollars, but instead
he chose to take thirty dollars for his ounce from a man
who drove out from town once a week. Tom once had
to bail Orlo out of jail after he had peppered a tourist's
car with number-two goose shot. The tourist had taken
his photograph and failed to give Orlo his standard

quarter (a box of twenty-five twelve-gauge two-and-three-
quarter-inch shells costs $3.80, or about fifteen cents per
shot) . When it finally came to trial, Orlo was acquitted.
Tom and Mary said they had to get uptown to go to the
theatre and left, just in time to miss Sam talking about
mercury's being a cumulative attritional poison of the
liver that, like lead and carbon tetrachloride, can be
absorbed through the skin (this was two years before it
showed up in fish) .

Sam is one of the most good-natured and generous
people I know, but he is forever coming up with the most
dismal facts and quotations (often with tattered newspaper clippings to justify them) , like, "Mayor Cavanagh,
shortly before Johnson's order (during the Detroit riot of
July, 1967) for the troops to move, said the city 'looked
like Berlin in 1945 or Warsaw after the ghetto uprising.
This is an explosion of the completely lawless element.' "
Or a quote from the Federal Water Pollution Control
Commissioner that 15,236,000 freshwater fish were killed
in this country by pollution during 1968, the largest
single instance being caused by a petroleum-refinery
overflow that killed 4,000,000 fish in the Allegheny River
at Bruin, Pennsylvania. For months he used to carry
around (tucked into a soft leather-bound edition of the
Oxford University Press *Greek Lyric Poems*) Robert
Lipsyte's *New York Times* story about Dick Tiger in his
since past big money years never spending his money
lavishly, but investing it in apartment buildings and
movie theatres in Lagos and Port Harcourt, Biafra. His
favorite newspaper clipping was from the *Harvard Crim-
son* from last spring (when the local police fulfilled a

century-old dream and got university permission to invade the yard) ; in the fourth column of a full-page story
in relating about the hundreds who had been arrested, it
said, "They are all being arraigned as indigents to speed
up the process." Sam is a reformed lush who hasn't had
a drink in eight years. He used to drink Crown Royal
Canadian, a thirty-five-year-old whiskey that came in a purple velvet sack with a serially numbered tag printed by the
Canadian Bank Note Company. It now comes in a purple
felt sack with an offset label, but Sam doesn't drink any
more, anyway. Despite the fact that he only drinks coffee,
Sam is always welcomed by any bartender who knows him
because he tips the same as if he were drinking booze.
Sam best exemplifies the skills of a city man—he can draw
just the needed amount of attention to himself without
ever losing grace.

One day in the winter of 1963–64 my mother called on
the phone to tell me about my brothers. My mother is a
chemist and my father a civil-liberties lawyer. Actually
I come from a long line of civil-liberties lawyers—my
uncle Phillip represented Rivera when Rockefeller hid
his Marxist mural, and my grandmother Becky had two
suitors both of whom were distant cousins of hers. They
both had the same first and last names, so to distinguish
between them when speaking, the family called them
Louie-the-*kenner* (smart Louie) and Louie-the-*schöner*
(handsome Louie) . Becky was a wise woman and so she
married Louie-the-*schöner*—Louie-the-*kenner* became the
noted civil-libertarian Louis Boudin. Eric was in jail in
Haywood County, Tennessee, charged with assaulting a
policeman with a poisoned rag. He had been leading an

orderly, nonviolent demonstration outside a courthouse
to petition for enfranchisement for tenant farmers. The
sheriff, who didn't know too much about modern techniques of crowd control, but had the apparatus, first set
dogs on the marchers and then, when a German shepherd
had my brother by the wrist on the ground, the red-neck
sheriff poured liquid tear gas on him, not understanding
that it was supposed to be vaporized first. Eric took a
handkerchief out to cover his nose and mouth. A deputy
took it away from him, which at the time struck Eric as
a petty sadism. In court the next day (where Eric appeared on a stretcher, thirty percent of his skin having
been burnt off by the tear gas, and with the whites of
both his eyes a brilliant undiluted red from being kicked
by the deputy as he lay on the ground) the handkerchief
was introduced into evidence as the weapon with which
he had attacked the officer. Eric had originally gone to
the South in 1961 to help set up a co-op home-industries
project for the manufacture of leather goods by tenant
farmers who had been displaced from their land when
they attempted to register to vote (a nice irony, since
Eric does not believe in choosing between the lesser of
two evils and so had never registered in N.Y.C. himself).
Mike, my younger brother, was in jail in Berkeley after a
Free Speech Movement demonstration at Sproul Hall.
At that time I was a mechanic in a foreign-car garage on
Eighty-third Street (actually a converted stable, it still
had a life-size bust of a horse as part of the mansard
coping on the fifth floor) and getting up and going to
work every day at 7:00 A.M.—which my mother gleefully
informed me made me the black sheep of the family. I

had given the matter of movement involvement some thought the year before and decided that I could only be a liability, since by no means did I consider nonviolence to be a proper comportment. (Eric, on the other hand, is the only truly nonviolent man I have ever met. One of the techniques that he involuntarily developed, that later became a standard subject in nonviolence workshops, was to apply Gandhian techniques to dogs. Whenever he was mauled by a sheriff's dog, Eric would not resist but just go limp and talk in a reassuring tone to the dog. The dogs, which usually held their captives by the wrist, would not let go, but they would apply no more pressure with their teeth than they deemed necessary for restraint.) Eric is much smarter than I am.

I finally decided that they were right (not about nonviolence) and stopped working at a legal job for other people. If you don't work for someone else in N.Y.C., quite likely what you do is illegal. (Most of the younger painters in N.Y.C. now use spray guns rather than brushes. When I was a shop foreman, I had to go down to the Municipal Building and lose a day's work to get a license from the Fire Department as a compressor operator, a process that required both a written and a verbal test. I know of no painter who holds, or actually has need for, such a license. But it is just one more way in which the government can coerce the people into working for someone else.) Painters and writers, at least since they have lived in cities, have been forced to be outlaws—Villon is the first and clearest example.

Let me make clear that there are certain kinds of criminal behavior that I don't consider admirable—like Texans swerving over to the wrong side of the road with their cars to run over wolves or the desecration of the North Slope to get out oil. I must admit that there are some crimes, that even though they are not simply the avoidance of bureaucracy, I greatly admire—mostly for their imagination. About ten years ago a man wearing the blue coverall uniform of the building custodial staff, in broad daylight, took a screwdriver and unhurriedly removed the large round polished-brass glass-covered matching nautical thermometer and barometer that were mounted just outside the street-entrance door to Abercrombie and Fitch. Several salespeople on the ground floor observed him and assumed that he was authorized to take them down for repair. Neither the workman (who was not an employee) nor the instruments (valued at about eighty-five dollars each) have been seen since. When Sam was out in Santa Cruz (which is 300 miles up the coast from Union Oil's offshore rigs in the Santa Barbara Channel), he wrote that he found scoters dying of petroleum poisoning right outside his door. Somehow there seems to be more than a quantitative difference between Standard Oil (N.J.) running a full-page ad on the last page of the first section of the November 13 *Times* headed, "Was it worth it?" (boasting about the *S.S. Manhattan's* round trip through the Northwest Passage), and Shackleton's classified ad in *The London Times* some seventy years ago, "Men wanted for Hazardous Journey. Small wages, bitter cold, long months of complete darkness, constant danger, safe return doubtful. Honor and recognition in case of success."

A municipal government views its own highest function

to be uniformity and codification, but even under
a reformer this amounts to coercion (N.Y.C. plants only
two kinds of official trees along its streets—Japanese
planes and ginkgos, but the ailanthus grows without
official sanction out of every unattended backyard crev-
ice). My father is Hungarian and chose to name me
Antol. The N.Y.C. Board of Health found this too difficult and so chose to standardize the spelling and my birth
certificate (which accurately reports that I was born at
11:36 A.M., 3/19/1936) gives my name as Anthony. I had
a friend once whose last name was Workman. The family's name in Russia had been something like Brunvitz,
but when his grandfather got to U.S. Immigration on
Ellis Island, the official understood only English plus a
smattering of Yiddish. The man—in terror that he would
be sent back—kept protesting *"Arbiter! Arbiter!"* and so
the new name.

Mickey came over with his always cold cup of black
coffee and sat down. There had been talk around Max's
for some months that he was planning to open a second
store uptown. He said that the new place had been
named, again by Joel, Max's Terre Haute—and asked me
to take the job of renovating the place, which was at
First Avenue and Seventy-third Street. He said he figured
there should be about five weeks' work, mostly carpentry
and some plumbing. There was an existing restaurant
there and mostly it would be a matter of making it less
decorative. We made an appointment to go uptown the
next day to look it over. The last time I had done any
work for Mickey was during the first week in June, re-
pairing extensive damage caused by a Memorial Day fire

in the rear second-floor dining room, which almost put
him out of business. I'm not sure what his reaction was
when I showed him a clipping from the June 2 *Wall
Street Journal* headed, "Retail Sales in Week Led Year
Ago," stating that general sales were five percent higher
than a like period the preceding year, and that "the
sharpest sales gain was nineteen percent, scored by the
lumber-hardware-farm equipment group, while the only
drop was a one-percent decline from a year earlier in bar
and restaurant volume."

THE FISHING AND HUNTING CLUB OF THE AIR

MY CHILDHOOD DICTIONARY (age six) gave definitions that were no more helpful (e.g., for "bucket" it said, "See pail," for "pail" there was an illustration and "See bucket") than my teacher's definitions. As a result, I am, as Diane wrote in some poem the title of which I can't remember, possibly the only motorcycle mechanic in the world with the thirteen-volume O.E.D. next to his favorite chair. I don't take too kindly to definitions without historical principles—that plus Skeat's and Trench's and Partridge's utter delight in using words, as contrasted with Onions's accurate pedantry.

When I was eight, I took my father's pistol (a Walther model-nine vest-pocket .25-caliber automatic) from the closet where he kept it locked up, loaded it (six rounds in the clip plus a seventh in the chamber) , put the safety on, and carried it in my pants pocket for thirty days. I never felt the need to show it to anybody at school or even to tell them after the fact that I had been so pre- pared. At the end of the month I unloaded it, put the cartridges back in the box from which they came, oiled the pistol and returned it to its shelf. Since the gun was only used for occasional plinking during the summers at my grandfather's farm, it was never missed. (This was during W. W. II, we used to place tomato juice cans on top of wooden fence posts in an unused pasture, Scotch-tape on newspaper photographs of Hitler, and use them as targets. A direct hit would make him spurt blood. I always shot at his forehead first so that he would still have blood left when shot in the throat.)

My grandfather (Louie-the-*schöner*) was an immigrant from Russia who had gone through the usual progression of jobs, but at the age of sixty when he still lived behind a small grocery store that he ran in Brooklyn, he decided he had had it with N.Y.C. and in the middle of the De- pression he bought a foreclosed one-hundred-eighty-acre dairy farm just outside of Monticello, New York. He was a barrel-chested old-time Socialist who always seemed to have stubble on his face and taught himself to be a farmer from U.S.D.A. pamphlets. Once late at night a man appeared at his door pleading that his car was stuck down the road and his babies were crying and could he buy some milk. My grandfather told him that it was illegal for him to sell raw milk. The stranger persisted and finally the old man said he would give him two quarts but wouldn't take any money. As soon as the milk changed hands the man informed my grandfather that he was a New York State Health Department inspector and presented him with a summons for selling un-Pasteurized milk, which already had his name typed in. Instead of just paying the fine, as was usual in such cases rather than lose time in court, the old man insisted on a jury trial. Monticello even then was a summer-resort community, but the year-round residents were mostly farmers, and his peers acquitted him after five minutes.

My father told me that the pistol had been a W. W. I officer's pistol to be worn concealed up the sleeve (in case of capture). It wasn't until three years later that I learned that he was wrong. The model nine didn't go into production until 1921 (the Treaty of Versailles prohibited Germany from making handguns of greater than .25 caliber). He was confusing it with the similar, but cruder, model five (like the model nine, it is only $3^{15}/_{16}$ inches long), which like all arms made during time of war did not approach civilian guns in quality of finish, closeness of operating tolerances or fineness of metallurgy.

Walther has consistently made the best automatic handguns in the world. The firm dates back to a medieval armor-makers guild in eastern Germany. To this day the PP (*Polizeipistole*) and the similar but smaller PPK (*Polizeipistole Kriminal*) are the world's finest concealable weapons (they were first introduced in 1929 and 1931 respectively). The *Heeres Pistole* (the military version of which is more commonly called the P-38) is by far the best military sidearm ever developed. By design it has far more inherent accuracy than any Browning

patent (the basis for almost all automatics made since
1911) and it can be totally field-stripped without using
tools.

After thirty days it was clear to me that I would never
have to kill a man, but that just as surely I would never
be able to establish my own criteria for right and wrong
by obeying the rules of others.

It is now six years since I have worked in a foreign car
shop. When I was doing that kind of work (this was
while I was still married), I could and did memorize with
no conscious effort every single nut and bolt size (including the thread pitch) for every application for every car
I worked on from Isettas to Lotuses. It wasn't until years
later that I realized that what I was doing was to jam my
head so as to avoid seeing with the clarity I had had when
I was eight (jam—in the sense that Russia and the U. S.
jam the radio broadcasts of each other's political propa-
ganda—not just cram full). I had settled into marriage
as an avoidance of living and quickly allowed my wife to
become a lush—which I refused to recognize. Right after
I got married I moved us (despite some real and justi-
fiable anxiety by my wife) out of N.Y.C. to a 2,700-acre
farm near the Delaware Water Gap, where I had gotten a
job taking care of machinery maintenance. I worked up
to eighteen hours a day at the farm and I now suspect
that she drank eighteen hours a day at home. (There had
to be some reason why it was so hard to teach an intelli-
gent woman how to drive a car.) There wasn't all that
much work to do on the equipment, so most of the time
I worked with the carpenter building a new barn. As
soon as the first hay cutting was in and the tractors were

free, we trenched out for the footing and foundation and
by the fall had a one-hundred-twenty-head double-row
stanchion barn pretty well enclosed. The only part we
didn't build ourselves was the silo. Silos come in kit form
from a firm in upstate New York. You order the size you
want several months ahead of the time you want it. The
manufacturer sends you a list of erectors in Pennsylvania
which you then write to and agree on a date. The day
chosen, a big Studebaker flatbed truck arrived laden with
all the pre-cut wooden parts and iron hoops plus three
generations of boys and men from one Amish family from
around Ephrata. In two and a half days they assembled
a silo thirty-five feet in diameter and seventy feet tall that
would have taken the carpenter and me at least a month.
(In N.Y.C. almost the only father-and-son construction
trade is the rooftop water-tank erectors, basically the same
as silo building, only in N.Y.C. it is done by Russian
Jews.)

The most awesome thing I ever saw was while I was
working on that farm. I was taking a second cutting of
hay from a twenty-acre field measuring approximately
two hundred by five hundred yards that ran adjacent to
a woods along one of its long edges. I had started around
the perimeter and was cutting in decreasing rectangles
towards the center. As the patch of standing grass got
down to about a half acre, I noticed that the grass was
moving about in a way that could not have been caused
by the wind. I shut down the tractor's engine and was
about to climb down when the patch of grass exploded
into a blur. Starting with field-mice and ending finally
with white-tail deer, the fur-bearing animals that had

been spread out over the twenty acres and had gradually compressed into the much smaller space as I robbed them of their hiding places in the tall hay broke their cover and radiated out across the hundreds of yards of flat mown hay heading for the woods or the surrounding uncut fields. They followed a rigid progression of size, the smallest first, field-mice, chipmunks, rats, red and gray squirrels, weasels, skunks, rabbits, hares, porcupines, opossums, raccoons, woodchucks, red and gray foxes, and finally white-tails. Before them all came the grasshoppers —in less than a minute it was over, there must have been thousands of them.

Anyway, between too much arcane knowledge and one black thought that I refused to think, I became a parasitic vegetable—as did my wife. It was not dissimilar from the kind of obfuscation that is now practiced by the N.Y.C. police. With the exception of those commands that nobody in a neighborhood can deal with directly (Manhattan Boro North, Manhattan Boro South, Special Events Squad and T.P.F.) which are still prominently labeled—N.Y.C. police cars no longer bear identification of their command. In the fall of 1969, when the new 1970 model-year Plymouth patrol cars first appeared, there were no precinct signs on the rear doors as before. Then the 1968 and 1969 cars still in service began to be re-painted, the identical green and black pattern as before, but with the old signs painted over black. In addition to the four extant "POLICE" signs, now where it used to indicate the precinct number it says "POLICE" again— any fucking dolt can tell it's a police car—accurate infor-mation to obscure reality.

There used to be a weekly radio program on WOR in

the early evening called *The Fishing and Hunting Club of the Air* which I listened to when I was ten. There was a panel of sportsmen who would be read questions sent in by listeners and who would then answer the questions and tell anecdotes about their experiences while fishing or hunting. Anybody whose letter was read on the air would receive a prize related to the sport he asked about. After a while I started sending in questions myself. They were always questions to which I already knew the answers. After four or five such letters' being ignored by the program, I went to the library out of a desire to lessen my own ignorance. In an old book on fishing tackle I found the two most closely related but distinctly disparate types of hooks pictured.

Just after New Year's an aerosol bomb of bug spray arrived addressed to me with a return-address label from the radio station. This was in 1947, right after the war, and aerosol bombs were still an expensive rarity. Instead of today's disposable cannisters with push-button tops, this was a miniature compressed-gas cylinder that must have weighed five pounds, fitted with a fancy brass needle valve that you turned two full revolutions in order to allow the spray to come out, and cost about six dollars. They were refillable for about two dollars if sent back to the factory. America had not yet learned about disposable litter, but it was already dispensing poisons that accumulate by geometric progression up food chains. I was ten years old and delighted, I had never heard of a food chain, much less thought that I was dooming the Antarctic penguins. My first real love had been the pair of giant pandas at the Bronx Zoo (acquired soon after Mrs. William H. Harkness brought the first panda to arrive in this country to the Brookfield Zoo near Chicago in 1937) and I didn't know I'd never see another one here, because they are now considered to be communists. I had gotten disgusted when none of my letters had been chosen and had stopped listening a month earlier. I assumed that it was some sort of Christmas present/consolation prize for my former persistence. About a week later a one-pound tin of Kentucky Club tobacco and two pipes arrived again with no cover letter. Within a few more days a large package containing a Martin automatic-rewind reel, one spool each of wet and dry line, and a Granger seven-and-a-half-foot three-section split-bamboo fly rod (with a spare tip section, hand-wound ferrules, and even a stainless-steel carrying case) arrived again with no letter. I told my father, whose office was in N.Y.C., and he went to WOR and had an acetate 78-RPM record cut (from the station's studio master) of the segment of the program that I had failed to listen to when they read my letter.

The record slipcase read: "Dynamic Recording Studios, 37 W. 57th St., New York 19, N.Y.—12/30/46 WOR EXCERPT FROM FISHING & HUNTING CLUB BROADCAST:

ANNOUNCER: What is the difference between a Limerick and a Carlisle hook? Is polar-bear hunting legal? Is an Army rifle a 30-30? To bring you the answers to these questions, together with many other interesting facts and stories pertaining to life in our great outdoors, the makers of Mail Pouch Chewing Tobacco and Kentucky Club Smoking Tobacco present The Fishing and Hunting Club of the Air, a program dedicated to good sportsmanship and to the conservation and propagation of our vast natural and wildlife

resources. So on behalf of Mail Pouch Chewing Tobacco
and Kentucky Club Smoking Tobacco we take you now to
the clubroom of The Fishing and Hunting Club of the Air.

CHAIRMAN: Good evening everyone and welcome to The Fishing and Hunting Club of the Air with Dave Mueller, sports-
man and author, Jim Haley of the *New York Daily Mirror,*
Don Hightower of *Field & Stream* magazine, and your
club chairman, Roland Winters, that's me. Now, before we
open tonight's program, thanks to everyone who sent us a
letter or postal card last week. We take this opportunity to
acknowledge them and want you to know that your questions, stories, and tips make up your program. So keep writing. Each week is a new contest and every week everybody
has an equal chance for such fine equipment as fishing rods,
reels, outboard motors, guns, hunting coats, boats. . . .

1ST VOICE: . . . I remember seeing old Kate bring in six birds
in one trip. [*Laughter.*]

2ND VOICE: Did she bring the basket around to the birds or
did she bring the birds to the basket?

1ST VOICE: Gran'pa always dropped them in one pile. [*Laughter.*]

2ND VOICE: You mean he shot them on the ground!

CHAIRMAN [*laughing*]:   Now, before somebody gives us the
bird, let's get to our next question, which is from Mr. A.
Weinberger of Great Neck, New York. Mr. Weinberger has
a question on fishhooks which wins for him a Granger fly-
rod, a can of Kentucky Club Smoking Tobacco, and a Martin
automatic flyreel. Here's his question: What is the difference
between a Limerick and a Carlisle hook?

1ST VOICE: Oh, there was an old gal from Dubuque . . . [*Laughter.*]

CHAIRMAN: Not that kind of limerick, Don. Can you answer
the question properly, Jim?

3RD VOICE: Yes. The difference is chiefly in the bend, really. The bend of your Limerick comes down in a high circle until just before the barb, then there's a sharp bend turning the point and barb up parallel with the shank.

CHAIRMAN: And the bend of the Carlisle hook?

3RD VOICE: The bend of your Carlisle is rounder all the way, more like the curve.

2ND VOICE: And the point of the Carlisle is always turned to one side while that of the Limerick is parallel to the shank.

3RD VOICE: Yes. Both are popular patterns, although the Carlisle is primarily for bait-fishing, while the Limerick is used chiefly for flies. Being most popular for salmon flies.

1ST VOICE: The bait fishermen like the Carlisle because it always has a long shank and it's easy to get out of the mouth of a fish.

3RD VOICE: That's right, Don. Sometimes the Limericks are made with long shanks, but usually not. Limericks are usually made with a turned-up or a turned-down eye and for salmon they're usually looped. But Carlisle hooks always are looped.

CHAIRMAN: Thank you, Jim. Now, here's a card from Mr. David Eldridge of Los Angeles, California, who asks: Is polar-bear hunting legal and if so why don't . . .

ANNOUNCER: . . . so send your letters to Fishing and Hunting Club, Mail Pouch Tobacco Company, Wheeling, West Virginia. Send your suggestions tonight. All material becomes the sponsors' property; in case of duplicates the earliest postmark wins, and the decision of the judges will be final. This is Tom Ready speaking for the Mail Pouch Tobacco Company of Wheeling, West Virginia, and this is the Mutual Broadcasting Network.

With the exception of the announcer, who sounded as if he were trying to sound like somebody else (the way

Carmine DeSapio does), they all had raspy whiskey voices.

I was quite a sullen boy and tended to walk on the public streets looking at my toes and the sidewalk cracks ("Step on a crack/break your grandmother's back"). I didn't learn much in school, or at least not the things they thought they were there to teach me. Mostly I learned about things, like not to chew on pencil erasers after putting them in my ear—nothing in the world tastes quite so bad as an eraser that you have just used to clean the wax out of your ears (from that I attempted to draw a tenuous equation of the words "ear" and "eraser"—I was forever trying to equate things with things, never people). Words themselves fascinated and often scared me. On opening day in the second grade (I had just been transferred to a different school when the districts for some reason had been gerrymandered), the new teacher told the boys to line up along the window wall, and the girls to line up along the opposite wall by the blackboards. Then she told the girls to go to the Home Economics room and the boys to go to Manual Training in the basement. We had to stand in the corridor for twenty minutes until the room was free. Waiting in an unfamiliar environment, I began to speculate as to what they had planned for me. I had never been in a class where the boys and girls were segregated before (I date my paranoia from that day). The teacher had said manual training—that had to mean training to be a man. Growing up in a suburban town I had little street-smarts and wasn't too sure what was different about boys and girls except that when they grew up they paired off—and I

wasn't about to let them train me in how to pair off, not
at seven years old. I am not sure if the relief of finding
out that manual training meant woodworking shop is
what led me to become a mechanic, but I'm certain that
I can date my enduring curiosity about etymology to that
twenty-minute wait.

I don't remember much of what happened (in school)
from then until I was twelve, when I was assigned to read
Homer. I started coming home every afternoon instead of
going out to the woods that ran from behind our house
down to the water where I had always played by myself
(there were subterranean concrete structures that I pre-
tended were enemy pillboxes to be captured, that
turned out to be leftover liquor caches used by Prohibition rumrunners). After about a week I came out of my
room and asked my mother what "rosy-fingered dawn"
meant. I'm still not sure I know—but I would now rather
sit in the woods and try to figure it out than play war.
What was much clearer to me about Homer was that even
if Odysseus was a con-man he was a good man because
one of his four bedposts was a live tree.

Most older N.Y.C. buildings have vaults (formerly used
as coal bins) extending out under the sidewalks. Leaving
the St. Adrian Company (a bar located in the Broadway
Central Hotel which was opened a little over two years
ago by Bruce Bethany, formerly Mickey's manager at the
Ninth Circle, which Mickey used to own, and Jerry
Houk, formerly the head bartender at Max's—it is named
after John Clark's back-bar mural, which is a repainting
of Frans Hals' group portrait as seen on a television
tube) the other night (still looking at my toes), I noticed

that the sidewalk vault ventilation grating in front of 661 Broadway (a loft building near Bond Street which must be at least seventy years old) is cast in the form of a series of parallel rows of geometric patterns, like the Aldermaston peace sign (which derives from the calligraphic symbols for the semaphore letters ND, meaning nuclear disarmament).

ANYBODY HERE WANT TO FUCK A POET?

WHEN I'M NOT either working or drinking I spend a lot of time wondering why America had to wait for the Spanish to bring over the horse from Europe when there used to be eohippai out West. I spend the rest of the time holding onto the end of my dog's nylon bone (real ones only last about half an hour under her scrutiny) wondering what Homer meant—"rosy-fingered dawn" and "wine-dark sea." But then I'm not very accomplished at getting drunk. What I am good at is drinking and talking to my friends as they get drunk. I rather envy the man who can drink with me for hours, shot for shot, and then stand up on the rung of a barstool so as to be taller than anyone else and call out, "Anyone here want to fuck a poet?" (which he is). I've never seen him do this when his wife is with him, but then I've never called out at all

and have no wife. It's the same sort of pragmatism as
Sam keeping two twenty-four-by-forty-eight-inch sheets of
expanded-metal plasterers' wire lath in the trunk of his
car in the winter to use if he gets stuck in the snow and
ice.

Writers or artists both initially sound the same in a
bar—they tell stories—that's what bars are for (it's certainly cheaper to drink at home). Bar stories which may
or may not be true (it is not significant, if the talk is
good—like the story about the Oscar awards in the mid-
fifties, when the name of the winning screenwriter was
announced nobody came forward and it became obvious
that it must have been a pseudonym for one of the black-
listed leftist writers, as the story goes it was Dalton
Trumbo, then living in Mexico, or the story that Mike
Nichols was fired years ago from a job as a waiter at the
Howard Johnson's at Sixth Avenue near Eighth Street
when he told a customer that that day's specialty was
chicken ice cream). I sometimes tell these stories to my
father, who is an often cantankerous, irascible man, but
one hell of a good lawyer. He says I should spend my days
in libraries instead of bars and says I learn my facts in the
gutter. An artist, like Ray, who calls himself a sculptor,
will talk in a bar so as to impress, as about his latest
project for which he has gotten two grants of three
thousand dollars each from the Yale Computer Center
(now he has to hire a programmer and an operator as
he knows nothing about computers). One is for a
schematic study of games theory as applied to N.F.L. football strategy and the other a movie made from barium-
series X-rays, both to try to design better center-city

traffic-flow patterns. But a writer, like Sam, will talk about
Lipton's use of the term "venereal" and contrast it with
Lawrence in *Studies in Classic American Literature,* who
puts down Ben Franklin for writing "rarely use venery"
and then adds, "And, by the way, I always thought books
on Venery were about hunting deer."

My father doesn't dislike stories, he just places too
much emphasis on truth and disparages verbal imagination. We were once vainly trying to establish the terms
of logic for an argument we were having, and to establish the absurdity of purity of facts I cited my birth certificate and said that even with its misspelling it was no
guarantee that I was that person or that my parents were
the people named (I wasn't particularly alluding to
bastardy) . He saved things from getting any worse between us by talking about the rules of evidence, which
are self-contradictory in that they deem as admissible
evidence only that to which the witness has first-hand
knowledge and yet will accept out of hand a witness's
testimony as to his name and place of birth. He thinks
me a miscreant for honoring Willie Sutton, but sent me a
clipping from the *Times* published a few days after
Sutton's release from Attica headed, "A Law Named for
Willie Sutton Assists Physicians" about a Dr. William
Dock who developed and espoused the method of skip-
ping over interim testing procedures so as to immediately
test for the most likely cause of symptoms ("Why do
you rob banks?" "That's where the money is.")

> In a telephone interview
> yesterday, Dr. Dock recalled
> that a young girl from Puerto

Rico had a mysterious liver
disease that puzzled Yale doctors. On teaching rounds Dr.
Dock extemporaneously suggested that the students and
internes follow what he
termed Sutton's Law.

Taking note of where she
had lived, Dr. Dock suspected
that the girl was afflicted with
schistosomiasis, a parasitic
disease common in Puerto
Rico and other areas of the
world. He recommended a
liver biopsy to establish the
diagnosis.

Many expensive blood tests
and time-consuming special
X-rays might have indicated
that the girl's enlarged liver
functioned poorly. After all
that, they still would not
have shown her physicians
that she had schistosomiasis.

An examination of a small
piece of her liver could do
that.

As it turned out the pathologist who examined the
biopsy tissue noticed nothing, but a medical student, on
reexamination, found eggs of the schistosome, thus vin-
dicating Dr. Dock.

The house I grew up in had eleven fireplaces. Before I
could get my allowance each week I had to build a fire
in each one. My father taught me the few physical skills
at which he was consummate—how to cook marrow bones

and goose *greben* (cracklings) and how to build a fire
using old newspapers instead of kindling under the logs
(we had an enormous supply of both soft and hard wood
logs, white pines blown down in the hurricane of 1947
and elms killed by Dutch blight). My mother and father
are getting old now and have moved back into N.Y.C.
and have no fireplaces. My mother, on the other hand,
taught me different things. She showed me that if you
remove a peanut from its seed pod, removed its red in-
tegumentary membrane, and carefully separated its two
cotyledons, that the exposed hypocotyl, radicle and plu-
mule formed the cowled, bearded face of a monk.

Ikons in botany—booze metaphors in the Vermont
shade, my back against a shagbark hickory, heels of
Vibram-soled boots caught on an outcropping of feldspar
(its right-angle cleavages making it ideal for Pennacook
arrowheads).

When I was twelve and thirteen I went to a Boy Scout
camp near Orwell, Vermont, located on a hogback between two lakes. There were still pileated woodpeckers,
mountain lions and black bears in the woods nearby.
There was no thought of danger, when you climbed a
rock wall you just never pulled yourself up by placing
your hand on a sunlit ledge higher than eye level—that
way you wouldn't disturb a diamondback out sunning
himself on the fractured micaceous feldspar on which
there were still visible the horizontal scrape marks of the
last Pleistocene glaciers. Most of the rock was gray, but
occasionally there would be a chunk that within one
square inch would vary from pyrites yellow to the red of
unclotted blood. The rock was so dense that even on the

hogback there was no way for sewage to drain off beneath the surface. We used lard soap, which is biodegradable, and at the beginning of the summer would dynamite holes for outhouses into the bedrock. Every day we would dump unslaked lime on top of the shit that had accumulated. If the hole filled up before the summer was over we would just cover it over with earth and blast a new one ten feet away. The counselors were all young veterans who couldn't find jobs after the war or who just wanted to get out of dreary jobs to spend a summer in the woods, none of them were professionals. The Army had been the strongest experience of their lives and they saw nothing either improper or unduly chancy in expecting a twelve-year-old to be able to learn to handle explosives. We in turn saw nothing improper in not mentioning it to our parents when they came to visit.

I suppose that the main thing that I learned as a boy was not to be categorized. (There seems to be an infinite number of ways to categorize. The man who launders my shirts doesn't read Arabic numerals very well. When I bring him the ticket, first he matches the color, changed every week, and then he looks for the right-hand-most of the three printed digits. He must have been in the laundry business for forty years, but he has never realized that in the West reading is done from left to right.) What I resent most to this day is not just that the government expects me to willingly pay them over a quarter of what I earn so that they can defoliate Asia (as well as a swath the length of the U.S.-Canadian border) , but that the smallest space to be filled in on the I.R.S. form 1040 is the one in the upper right-hand corner of the first page where it says "occupation"—as if anyone could state that in one word.

A couple of months ago Sam told me he had seen a filler story in one of the San Francisco papers that the Boy Scouts in Claysworth, Iowa, had volunteered to pick all the wild marijuana that was growing locally. They gathered over eight tons, which was then destroyed by the authorities. One of the boys was quoted as pondering what it would bring if sold on the streets in N.Y.C. Those kids will totally subvert the disposable-packaging manufacturers if they ever apply their imaginations to pop-top beer cans. (Jack London, writing about the scarcity and expense of supplies beyond the Chilcoot Pass during the 1898 gold rush, described how they would never throw out an empty beer bottle but would take a kerosene-soaked string, tie it around the bottle just below the neck taper and ignite it. At just the right moment they would plunge it into cold water and the bottle would crack in two along the line where it had been heated. Then they would take the bottom half and rotate the sharp edge back and forth in a bucket of sand until the lip of the newly formed tumbler was smooth enough to drink from.) A few more years and those kids will be standing on the rungs of barstools.

BOILER PLATE

THE BEST GRAFFITI I ever saw was written in
three different hands on the wall of the men's room of
the old Cedars in 1961. It said:

> Lumumba Lives!
> In Scarsdale.
> With Your Mother.

Mickey and I went uptown to the southwest corner of
First Avenue and Seventy-third Street to his new store. It
had been a singles bar named Graffiti. The decoration
had been huge photographic blow-ups of wall scrawlings,
(the only ones that seemed to show any imagination by
the photographer were of two notices posted by building
superintendents:

NOTICE

Who is the wise one who messes up
this sign. Just dont get causht at it.

Yoo are told not to leave Anything on the
Floor for pickup on sundays or holiday's.
Yet someone does not read of can-not
read. Once more I ask you to put out
Your trash before <u>9a.m.</u> monday's through Sat's
except sundays or holiday's.
Try to keep this floor clean after using the
incinerator. <u>Thank you.</u>

<u>Supt.</u>

for some of the tenants that when
   needs electric bolbs in his——
apartment use to take it from the
hall away Ill. apreciate dont.doit
any more
               Thank you the Super.)

Every table had a twelve-by-eighteen-inch piece of slate
and some chalk, and the bathroom walls were painted
flat black so the patrons could exercise their egos (e.g.,
"Sirocco blows," "Mike's bag is brown paper"). The
place had been owned and built by Mike Steinberg, who,
I think, enjoys building restaurants more than operating
them. He is now building a place directly across the
street called The Laundry Bag, which is to be a combination restaurant and laundromat. I don't think it will
make it—at best the regular customers will come in only
once a week.

Mickey wanted to rip out all the stained-glass panels
(complete with heraldic escutcheons), the tapestried
hanging room dividers, the random-pattern bricks pro-

truding in relief from the stucco south wall, the non-
functional brick fountain (complete with plastic tropical
leaves—which turned out to be rented—after I had thrown
them out in the refuse scow), the raised stage in the back
room (on which they had held amateur improvisational
skits), and the ornate cast-brass Japanese imitation-
antique hanging ceiling fixtures and wall sconces. The
woodwork was as well done as that in any bar that Otto
Jacoby has ever built (Bradley's on University Place and
Tenth Street, The Lion's Head on Sheridan Square, &c.)
with random plank-width Australian oak pegged flooring,
a truly magnificent (if somewhat rickety) seventy-foot-
long mahogany bar complete with beveled back-bar
mirrors, coolers with inset panels of Tennessee brown
marble, and simple cast-brass hardware on all the drawers
and back-up bottle storage cabinets (it had come out of
one of the old hooker bars on Broadway in the mid-
Forties which had been torn down for a new tinted-glass
and anodized-mullion office building), and well-done
incidental carpentry work (like the coatroom, bus stands,
&c.) in four-inch tongue-and-groove wainscoting with
pegged T-bar mouldings. There was a full basement
which contained an office, a liquor room and a walk-in
beer cooler and absolutely no shelf storage space for
linen, glassware, crockery or food. The kitchen was
smaller than in a one-family house built before W. W. II.

Mickey had hired a general contractor who got permits
for all the work and supplied the scow. For once in my
life I was going to do a job without a boss (Mickey being
too busy trying to rebuild Kansas City's business after the
fire, and smart enough to leave me alone) and yet legally,

but it did mean I had to get an alarm clock, since my hours were fixed by the lumberyard and other suppliers' delivery drivers. Each morning I would get there at 7:30 A.M., and work until 4:30 P.M., when I would go back downtown to Kansas City to eat and drink.

I could usually depend on Semenovich to be there by the time I arrived. Semenovich is the only Serbo-Croatian I've ever met (he says *"Nasdróbia,"* at the Chit-Chat they say *"Násdorov"*—that is, if he's being cordial—other times he says things that I think mean something like "Your mother makes it with toothless horses") . He is forever getting into scams so that he won't have to keep working for his father as the East-coast representative for a Mil-waukee-based company that makes babbitt-metal bearings. He recently took the option to buy twenty thousand used bowling balls. He had met a man in an uptown bar who told him that he had them for sale. They took a cab out to Red Hook to inspect them. In the warehouse, which Semenovich claims was dimly lit by fifteen-watt bulbs hanging down on wires from the ceiling, the balls were stacked in pyramids like cannonballs at a restored Revo-lutionary War fort. Most bowling balls are made of a black phenolic plastic similar to Bakelite, which has little if any scrap value. Some are made of Lucite, and a few of cork. Semenovich claims that in the dim light he saw a high percentage of clear Lucite balls, which would bring a good return if sold for scrap, but that the stacks near the door must have been salted with these. The price was five cents each plus accrued storage charges. The balls were all chipped and had been traded in by bowl-ing alley operators on new balls, and had no value other than that of the materials from which they were made. He paid a thousand dollars for the option on the lot but could not remove them until the storage lien was paid. On closer inspection there turned out to be only sixty-three Lucite balls, and no market for the rest of them. It also turned out that to crate them for shipping would cost more than he had already paid, since a bowling ball weighs about sixteen pounds and must be packed quite securely, rolling around loose, they will break open any container. A few years back automotive writers used to facetiously measure the trunk capacity of cars (which had a relatively high cubic-footage figure for available stowage space, but so broken up by the spare tire, the rear shelf deck, and the space under the rear fenders that the actual space usable for ordinary luggage was a much lesser figure) by the number of ping-pong balls that could be stored in them. Semenovich had heard that Larry Rivers, the painter, had gotten a hundred-thousand-dollar grant from the de Menil Foundation in Houston to do a project on black history in America. He said he was going to try to talk Rivers into taking the bowling balls off his hands to use for a road-gang tableau. I doubt he will even try.

In the early 1900s it used to take six or seven days for a new joke to travel from one coast to the other by salesmen's word of mouth. Once the wire-service teletype machines went in the time lapse dropped to three hours (the maximum time gap between hard-news stories). Semenovich is always the first person to tell a new joke, but they always sound as if they originated in Milwaukee and as if I had heard them before—they always hinge on

verbal distinctions (what is the difference between a
group of midget sprinters and a group of women athletes?
Well, one is a bunch of cunning runts . . . or, what is
the difference between an American rabbit and a French
rabbit? Well, an American rabbit goes hippety-hop, and
a French rabbit goes lickety-split.) He lives by himself in
a long, narrow loft on Hester Street which we sometimes
use for archery practice. There always seems to be something makeshift about him, like taking his shirts to the
laundromat to be washed and then only ironing the col-
lar and cuffs and wearing them under a sweater.

The closest Semenovich ever came to making money
from one of his schemes was several years ago when he
got the idea to corner the world market (exclusive of the
U.S.A., where the Audubon Society had their importa-
tion outlawed over fifty years ago) on penguin pelts.
Thousands of penguins are slaughtered annually by the
Indians at Tierra del Fuego (seventy-five years ago
Joshua Slocum, while sailing alone around the world in
the *Spray,* wrote of "the treachery of these cunning
savages" and placed carpet tacks on his deck while he
slept, to act as caltrops), who pummel them to death for
the meat (which they sell for dog food) and throw away
the hides. Unlike other birds, penguins have fur, not
feathers. So he figured a new type of fur would bring a
premium price. He formed a syndicate which had made
preliminary contacts with a government official in Ar-
gentina. Then the government changed hands and the
deal fell through. (Every summer two-thirds of the
world's northern fur seals land at the St. Paul Island

rookeries in the Pribilofs off the west coast of Alaska to whelp and then breed five days after the young are born. The island has a population of four hundred Aleuts, the largest remaining settlement of an otherwise vanished people, who are all employed by the U. S. government, which owns the Pribilofs. By international treaty pelagic seal hunting, which is less efficient, is outlawed. Each year about one and a quarter million fur seals land on the island's rock-strewn shore. Of these between forty and eighty thousand young bulls which are not yet big enough to establish harems against the domination of the older bulls are clubbed to death by the Aleuts. The pelts are brought to the annual fur auctions in N.Y.C. and sold by the government to furriers. The meat is ground up and sold as ranch-mink food, also by the government. There is no free enterprise on the island, with one exception—a man named Alexander Melovidov sells dried seal cocks for half a dollar each to an aphrodisiac merchant in Brooklyn. No doubt with U. S. foreign-aid assistance to underdeveloped countries, the Indians of Tierra del Fuego will soon achieve the same efficiency.)

Semenovich is now working on a plan to market an instant energy drink that is made from a complex series of nitrates that, to my sometimes ill-remembered knowledge of chemistry, sound like fertilizer by-products. It does give quick energy; the only real problem he has is that it tastes like Mil-Organite (a biodegradable fertilizer that the city of Milwaukee sells at a profit, made from processed sewage, Milwaukee is the only city in the country that seems to be able to do this—the only appreciable

distinction that I can make out is that they have a higher
percentage of beer in their piss) . It will probably get as
far as most of his scams.

I have never mentioned any subject to him that
he didn't come up with an unlikely story. I once asked
him what he thought it would have felt like to be a pilot
committed to a final approach to Idlewild at 5:28 P.M.
on November 8, 1965. He immediately answered that all
the bearing companies had made a great deal of money
from the blackout. Even Con-Ed couldn't conceive that
one yard circuit breaker overloading in Ontario could
cause such a geometrically progressive mess. For several
minutes they kept their generators turning, forgetting
that the bearing-lubrication pumps were driven by electric motors and had failed, allowing the oil film to rup-
ture on all the journals and the bearings to fuse with the
shafts. Even a highly polished metal surface such as an
armature's shaft is highly abrasive (like the magnified
pictures of the edge of a razor blade in a Gillette television commercial) and the function of a lubricant is to
maintain a sliding film, measured in ten-thousandths of
an inch, between the hardened metal of the shaft and the
relatively soft metal of the babbitt bearing.

One day when I got off work at Terre Haute (which
Joel insists should be pronounced "terry hut") , Julie was
at Max's downtown, just in from Burlington, where he
had been working as part of a research project being run
by the University of Vermont on the protein content in
sugar-maple sap. Sap for maple sugar and syrup is no
longer collected in individual buckets from each tree in
a sugarbush. It is now drawn under high vacuum directly

into the boiling vats through miles of manifolded plastic tubing, so that one man can now operate a four-thousand-tree grove. The greatest hazard to the operator is no longer the cold weather, but whether stray snowmobiles cut the hoses or pull out the bungs from the trees. Julie had nothing but bad-mouth for what was being done by farmers who were trying to get a higher short-term yield from their trees knowing that their sons would not continue to operate their farms after they died. Irritating devices similar to intra-uterine devices were being used to keep the bung holes open for longer periods and the tappings themselves were being treated with paraformaldehyde (an irritant that keeps the scar from healing over) for the same purpose. It was at first thought that since the sap yielded had a higher protein content it might be more nutritious, but on closer examination Julie found under an electron microscope that the proteins that were being stimulated (probably by the vacuum) were phenolics, which are thought to be indigestible.

Julie started telling of watching the Orange Bowl game on television, sponsored by DuPont. One of the commercials during half time was about their efforts to develop a chemical that would make all the oranges fall off the trees at the same time so that manual fruit pickers could be eliminated and a machine could harvest the crop. What the commercial failed to mention is that the auxins (regulatory plant hormones) that they were isolating, called abscisons, which control the formation of the corky abscission layer between the petiole and the branch, are the same class of product that they are developing for the military for use in wholesale defoliation

of entire forests thought to contain hostiles. (Despite my
obvious irrationality, I admire the DuPont Company for
its past achievements. When I was a boy, I picked up an
early nineteenth-century DuPont gunpowder cannister. It
was of the approximate size and shape of a pint hip flask
of whiskey but made of painted tin-plated iron with a
pasted-on ornately printed paper label. It was painted
British racing green and must have been at least one
hundred thirty years old, quite some time before the development of synthetic aniline dyes. The color after so
many years was still mint bright. As late as the 1860s
Lincoln was criticized by fashionable people in Washington because his suit was old and so the originally black
organic dye had started to fade towards green. Even today
the high-grade industrial green paints that Frank Stella
used for some of his rainbow-shaped canvases have been
known to change hue. I'm not sure why the paint color
on that old powder cannister lasted so long, but the same
care that went into its development is now going into
irreversible destruction.) Julie had quit the job in Burlington and come back to N.Y.C. looking for work, saying
he would never again live in a place where all the stores
carried was flannel bread and the people didn't laugh at
the same dialogue in a movie that he did.

I hired Julie on as an assistant and we started work
building a walk-in cooler for vegetables and meat in the
basement. A walk-in box is actually a room-sized refrigerator made of two-by-six framing with two-by-four stag-
gered studding covered with marine-grade plywood with
the hollow space between the interior and the exterior
walls filled with fiber-glass insulation. While we were

building it, Chris Jebb, the manager of Thursday's, came in one day about noon looking quite shaken. Chris used to visit almost every day and we would go over to his place, which doesn't really open until 6:00 P.M., to drink before going to one of the neighborhood Czech restaurants for lunch. Early the preceding morning, some time after closing at 4:00 A.M., someone had broken into Thursday's through the rear window, gone to the office in the basement and wheeled the safe from there into the adjacent walk-in box. Inside the insulated room they could take their time, where nobody could hear them, as they drilled open the safe and made off with $4,000. Julie and I took on a side job that evening setting the new safe into a concrete block which we doweled with half-inch reinforcing rods into the concrete floor of the basement. That way, if anybody tried again, it couldn't be rolled away and they would have to work on it where the noise could be heard. Supermarkets have the best system—they mount their safes to the floor right in plain view with the safe door facing the front window, so that anybody passing on the sidewalk can see if it is being tampered with. Julie had found forty-seven acres of woodlot near Chester Depot, Vermont, on Trebow Road (at one time all the land around there was cleared of its original tree cover, but the name still survives from the practice of New England Indians who would bend over and tie a sapling so that its trunk was horizontal to the ground at a height of about three feet, as the supple young trunk would turn upwards again seeking the sunlight, a bowed tree, something like one branch of an *espalier,* would grow as a marker for deer trails) with a fine swift trout

stream cutting through it. I gave Emil Mattson, the
owner, a deposit on it and started working on as many
side jobs as I could get to pay off the land and pick up a
used four-wheel-drive truck.

While still working on Terre Haute days I took a job
rewiring a loft for a waitress at Max's named Karen. The
loft was on the top floor of a building in the middle of
the wholesale flower district on Twenty-sixth Street near
Sixth Avenue. Like most top floor lofts it had skylights
and they leaked. After I had finished the wiring I built
two six-foot by eight-foot twenty-gauge copper pans which
she put on the floor directly under the skylights and used
for rock gardens, getting slightly withered plants free from
merchants in the neighborhood. Waitresses at Max's are
expected to supply their own short all-black dresses, which
some of them refer to as their mini-nun uniforms. (From
the July 6, 1968 *New York Times:*

MINISKIRTS HAVE BEEN SLIPPING BY BRITISH SALES TAX

London, July 15, UPI—
Miniskirts are more than just
provocative, according to
British revenue authorities—
they are tax evaders as well.

In fact, they are depriving
Her Majesty's Treasury of
thousands of pounds every
year in purchase taxes.

A tax official explained that
a 12½-percent purchase
tax is charged only on skirts
longer than 24 inches from
waist to hem. Anything

shorter is classified as children's clothing and hence,
is not taxable.

As all young—and not-so-
young—ladies know, 24 inches
is almost a maxi. Standard
mini lengths run from about
13 to 20.

Several plans for raising the
hem on the taxable limit have
been proposed, but nothing
definitive is yet in view, the
official said.

"Something will be done
and soon," he added, "but I
can't yet say just what.")

Most of the girls adorn their somewhat drab outfits with
Moroccan jewelry, except Karen, whose grandmother was
a Mormon who collected but wouldn't wear Zuni and
Hopi turquoise and silver corn-blossom necklaces which
she inherited. She claims she was born in a log cabin, but
then again so does LaMonte Young. LaMonte is an
electronic composer who is so obsessed with the origi-
nality of creation that he even insists on putting a ©
symbol on the Christmas cards he and his wife send out
each year. He believes that our lives are so thoroughly
imbued with sixty-cycle oscillations from the hum of re-
frigerators, electric clocks &c. that all of his music, which
resembles droning ragas, is either at sixty cycles or one or
more of its multiples. Several years ago he wanted a cube
that would incorporate a tone generator which would
emit two frequencies, sixty and nine hundred sixty cycles
in overlapping sine waves, and that would display calli-

graphic patterns by his wife, Marion Zazeela, on each of
the five visible sides. An audio engineer named Futterman
built the tone generator into a rectangular chassis about
four inches by five inches by eight inches. I designed and
built a cube for him that would hold the tone generator,
allowing ample room for both cooling and adjustment of
the controls, and at the same time supply evenly dis-
tributed edge lighting to the five Day-Glo green and pink
panels from twelve black-light fluorescent fixtures of eight
watts apiece. All of this in a fourteen-inch square cube
with no visible hardware or means of attachment. It was
shown at the MOMA Art and Technology show (it was
one of the very few devices that, when I went to the show,
didn't have an "Out of Order" sign on it) with no credit
given for design or construction only for the music and
drawings. I think Tinguely is right—the next time I build
an object for an artist, I'm going to build in an auto-
destruct system that, when it's done, will spell out
"THANK YOU" in red smoke.

The size of the kitchen at Terre Haute was fixed because all four of its walls bore structural weight, it was
tagged onto the rear of the restaurant like an afterthought.
Rather than go to the great expense of putting in steel
girders to support the upper floors of the building so as
to be able to open out the kitchen, we built a pantry and
salad room adjacent to the extant kitchen and an additional food-preparation room in the basement with provision for cutting and washing vegetables and butchering
meat.

Tony Gould, who used to be the manager of Kansas
City, but who had taken the job of managing St. Adrians

about a year ago, was supposed to take the job of managing Terre Haute. A week before the scheduled opening
date he changed his mind and decided to stay downtown,
where he felt more familiar. Mickey asked me how I'd
like to run the place, saying he had great respect for my
organizational abilities. I think what he had in mind was
to always have a plumber on hand in the middle of the
night. I was somewhat skeptical about having a boss
again, but the idea of having a bar that was mine to do
with as I pleased won out and I took the job (the pay,
including all I could eat and drink, was almost as good
as I could make working with my hands), on the condi-
tion that if it wasn't working out, either one of us could
call it with no hard feelings. The last thing to arrive just
before opening was a brand-new jukebox that would accept dollar bills (twelve plays for a dollar, but only eight
plays for four quarters). The first thing I did was try one
of the replica bills with Dick Gregory's picture instead of
Washington's that he had used as political handbills when
he ran for president. It worked just fine. I should have
realized then that I was not of the right temperament to
be a restaurant manager. I had figured that I would have
lots of time to talk to my friends at the bar, but most of
the time I was concerned with what my father calls
"boiler plate" (an old-fashioned lawyer's term for the
standard reused portions of a printed contract—it probably derives from a printer's term for rotary-press plates
that are curved and resemble miniature boiler plates)
and had little time for much else.

STEAK LOBSTER CHICK PEA

In 1863 the Indian fighter Colonel Richard Irving Dodge, from the top of Pawnee Rock in Arkansas—"I could see from six to ten miles in almost every direction. This whole vast space was covered with Buffalo, looking at a distance like a compact mass," and again, in 1871 Dodge rode for three days through a herd of bison that he estimated to be twenty-five miles wide and fifty miles long and containing over four million head. It became expedient to exterminate the bison in order to subvert the plains Indians. Bison, unlike the longhorns and later whiteface or Herefords that replaced them, are naturally adapted to plains existence, being able to graze under the drifting snow. By 1895 only some eight-hundred-odd bison were left in the United States. The few bison that remain belong to the Department of the Interior which periodically opens restricted hunts to keep down the size of the herd. I heard of this and wrote the Department to ask if they would let me have one (or preferably a pair) if I

138

would supply adequate grazing land for the beasts. I got back a letter from a sub-undersecretary (presumably in charge of nuisances) saying that the bison belonged to the American people and that I could only have one if I were a municipal zoo. I am not, but I am an American until or unless some department decides otherwise, and cannot see that a bison is better off being shot or living in a cage.

Anyway, I was working for Mickey to pay off Mattson so as to be able to get out of N.Y.C. In 1874 Congress passed a bill "to prevent the useless slaughter of buffaloes within the Territories of the United States" which Grant pigeonholed. Nixon isn't even a drinker. I'd just as well live within walking distance of even a defoliated border rather than on an island. (I have lived on the Lower East Side for some seven years now and there are things about this neighborhood that I will miss, despite its poverty and crime, like the old-fashioned patent medicines that can still be found in the pharmacies here. Last year I gave myself a unilateral inguinal hernia while bulling a cast-iron bathtub up three flights of stairs. After I got out of the hospital where they sewed me up, I went into a drugstore to fill a prescription for Valium, a mild muscle relaxant that the surgeon had told me to take for a month so that I wouldn't rip myself open again. The pharmacists here are so leery of heads looking to get something to get high on that they treat even the most innocuous prescription as though you had asked them for a ten-percent tincture of cocaine hydrochloride. While the pharmacist was in the rear of the store telephoning my doctor to verify the prescription, I started to read the labels on the

boxes of patent medicines in an unlocked glass case. One
of them was called "Lee's Save-The-Baby." On the side
panel of the box it said, "For Children and Adults. May
be used Internally and Externally according to the Direc-
tions contained herein. The name 'Save-The-Baby' is not
intended to imply that the product will 'save babies,' but
rather that it is efficacious in those conditions for which
it is recommended." It has been made at Watervliet, New
York, since 1874 and contains 3.3 percent U.S.P. alcohol
by volume as well as "an excellent mixture containing
canada balsam, camphor, oil origanum, and oil rosemary,
incorporated in a suitable lard base." I also found Min-
ard's Liniment, made in Hyannis, Mass., with a picture on the box of what I take to be a crowned and
bearded nineteenth-century Bohemian king wearing an
ermine robe over one shoulder and holding a scepter in
his left hand. The scepter in the left hand, like the bar-
sinister in heraldry, implies that he descends from a bastard branch of the family, but I choose to believe that the
pained look on his face is caused by dyspepsia, which
will be cured when he takes the mustard-colored medicine
containing "muriate of ammonia, camphor, turpentine,
soap and stronger ammonia water." The label is printed
by offset lithography, but appears to be a reproduction
from an original steel engraving. I bought a bottle of each
and then went back to check the label on Lydia E. Pink-
ham's Vegetable Compound but found that they have up-
dated it—a few years ago you could still find fly-specked
boxes that listed among its numerous ingredients ground
horn or both true and false unicorn. Two blocks south of
this pharmacy is the store where I buy my bib overalls

and steel-tipped Herman's work shoes. Over the last four years I have installed hundreds of new toilets—and shit in every one of them to test the flushing mechanism and drainage. But it was Mr. Simon, who runs the work-clothes store, who pointed out to me a phenomenon I had never taken note of—that in the northern hemisphere all sink, bathtub and toilet vortices swirl counterclockwise, and vice-versa in the southern hemisphere—apparently it is a function of the magnetic field.) Peter Matthiessen points out that all North American imperiled or extinct creatures shared two habits—"They were localized or un-common before the white man affected them, and they were unadaptable to change," but as good a writer as he is he is willing to accept the bison at a "safe level." The miners following the 1849 gold strike almost extinguished the California condor (an Eocene anachronism, the Thunderbird of Indian mythology, with a ten-foot wing-span of which at last count, in 1959, fewer than sixty examples survive—none in municipally owned zoos) in whose huge quills they stored and carried their gold dust.

I'm not at all certain why Mickey felt the need to open another store. I suppose that anyone running a retail oper-ation does it to make money. All my life I have been fascinated more by gold rushes than by gold. In the winter of 1897 there was seventy feet of snow in Alaska. To even make the attempt the law required a year's sup-ply of provisions, one ton per man. The lowest crossing of the St. Elias Range was at Chilcoot Pass, six thousand feet above sea level at Juneau. A man had to make thirty successive trips to the top to pack his outfit up—burying each sixty-five-pound load in the snow at the top. There

was much stealing of food. From there he had to sled
overland to Bennett Lake, where he had to build a boat
out of green frozen wood caulked with boiled spruce gum
that would be strong enough to shoot the Whitehorse
Rapids. The first week in June 1898, the ice cleared the
Klondike River and the rush towards Dawson began. One
hundred thousand set out, thirty thousand reached Dawson, four thousand found any gold, three hundred became
rich from mining. Half of the men reaching Dawson
never tried their hands in the creek beds; they just came
and went home, straight down the Yukon River to the
ocean on hundreds of stern-wheeled steamships. In four
years it was all over. I'm not certain what I would have
done—probably built sluices and bars.

　I was the only Tony in the town where I grew up and
overly conscious of the ethnically incongruous juxtaposi-
tion of my first and last names. From the age of six or
seven I knew I would live in N.Y.C.—I saw my name as
"to N.Y." My heroes, except for criminals, were not city
men—Liver-Eatin' Johnson (the Crow killer) , Henrik
Carlsen (the captain of *The Flying Enterprise*) , Joshua
Slocum, and Sequoya (a half-breed Cherokee who devised
a syllabary for his tribe, the only Indian language that
can be written—the redwood tree was named after him) .
Being Hungarian, the Cherokees and their language
have always fascinated me—the word "Cherokee" is
thought to derive from the Creek word *"tciloki,"* which
means "people of the aberrant speech." If you know you
will always be looked upon as aberrant in speech or
thought patterns, then you know you must be able to
move and have a trade. Sam frequently cites Homer to me

that the four kinds of outlanders that you don't exclude
from your state are the seer, the doctor, the poet, and the
maker of tools and weapons. Still a valid criterion, it
makes William Carlos Williams and George Oppen the
great men of America. But Williams said the pure products of America go crazy and went through the motions
of toasting the Father of His Country with an empty
bottle (Prohibition: 1927) and said booze was the only
evidence of God in this environment (and Flossie says
HUAC killed him, calling him un-American while not
bothering to read *The Pink Church,* afraid of the word),
and Oppen went mute for twenty years, forced into exile
in Mexico, rather than be misread. George once told
Diane that when he decided to start writing poetry again,
he began what eventually became the book *The Materials*
by making up a list of all the plumbing fixtures in his
house. No, I'll work for a while for a boss to buy my way
off this island. Williams told me a poet must live along
the littoral, perhaps I mistook his word.

Friends would come in on Monday nights (always the
slowest night in the bar business) and talk. Diane just
back from a reading tour in California describing a three-
night and two-day train trip (in the 1950s when Young
was waging a proxy fight to take over the New York
Central Railroad, he ran a full-page ad in the *Times* to
the effect that hogs could travel coast to coast by train
undisturbed but that people had to change trains in
Chicago—they still do), or Charles Lowrey to talk about
side-hill mules and the five-gaited walking horses from his
youth in Sparta, Tennessee—suddenly switching to talking
of how this country habitually overproduces and yet the

U. S. Post Office (probably the most inefficient in the
Western world) uses a low-grade jute cord (about the
type that you would expect to find in a hardware store
in Portugal) to bundle mail that is precisely strong
enough to hold the bundles together well and yet easily
snapped with the bare fingers as the carrier distributes
letters to the battery of individual mailboxes in an apartment house, or Jerry Brewster, a frame maker, disgusted
with the preceding day's football game bitching that if
there were a fifteen-yard penalty for dry-humping the
center, the Giants would hire a faggot quarterback.

The bar had been open for three months before
Mickey got around to having a sign put up. When Joel
was at Black Mountain College he learned to be a
printer while putting out well printed and bound edi-
tions of some of the best poetry this country has produced.
He now makes his living as a free-lance production man.
He taught Joe the same trade, which consists mostly of
bringing a good eye to the total of print, space and what
there is to be said (or shown). When Mickey opened
Kansas City, some five years ago, Joel designed the logos
and chose the font that has become synonymous with
Max's. Mickey believes in not changing once he has found
a workable system, so the same type font had to be used
on the uptown sign. (It is a distinctive face, I've only
seen it used for a sign one other time and that on one of
those "antiques" stores on Second Avenue that sells
stripped Cedar Rapids oak furniture. The type face is
called Windsor and was first listed in the Stephenson-
Blake catalog in 1923. There are capital letters listed but
Joel used only the lower case, which has oblique serifs

and very short descenders. The "a" is distinguished by a
large bowl and the "e" by an oblique stroke to the eye.
The "m" and "n" are splayed as is common with "k."
The "s" and "x" have serifs like the upper case. It is
generally classified as a "display roman," and is not suitable for book texts.) Joel doesn't talk much about his
work, but Joe will sometimes bring in a trade paper with
ads like the one from Hammermill Paper Company with
bound-in samples of two sixty-pound book papers, one
a fairly highly calendered English finish and the other a
glare-free paper in the identical off-white. The text states
that the gloss paper bulks at five-hundred-sixty pages per
inch, while the other paper of the same weight bulks at
two-hundred-seventy-six pages per inch, and advises that
by proper selection a three-hundred-page novel can be
made to look more impressive or a five-hundred-page
paperback can be made more handy. Bob Creeley, in a
tape from a poetry conference in Vancouver in 1963, talks
of the first time he visited Dr. Williams in East Ruther-
ford and Williams showing him upstairs to the room
where he had his typewriter and the prescription pads
that he wrote on. The size of the paper prescribing the
poems. (Diane has been using a shorter, less cumbersome
line since she now often writes first drafts on the backs of
envelopes on planes and trains and not just on a typewriter.)

Everybody I know who met Williams remembers their
first meetings. Gil talks of walking in the front door
(which opened directly to the base of a flight of stairs
that bent at a right angle halfway up) just as Williams,
who must then have been in his mid-seventies, got to the

landing—and Williams telling Gil's wife, Elsene, not to
move, he wanted to look at her body. Gil was working
for a book publisher at the time and used to make copies
of his poems on the company Thermo-Fax machine. By
that time Williams' hands shook so badly from the stroke
he had after being subpoenaed by Congress that he could
not read a sheet of paper that he was holding, so Flossie
would read to him. She got an allergic reaction to the
chemicals in Thermo-Fax copying paper. Both because
of their health and to hear the voice, he would ask young
poets to come out to visit and to read their work to him.
I remember he had a big atlas on the table in front of
the couch where we sat and every time I mentioned a
place, he would make me find the appropriate map and
show him precisely where it was. I was talking about
climbing a rock chimney up the east slope of a twelve-
thousand-foot peak in Estes National Park in Colorado
and how just before I got to the top there was an eagle's
nest blocking the ascent. I had had to work my way down
several hundred feet and try a different route to the top.
While I was going up, I hadn't been able to see the eyrie
until I almost shunted it with my head. The birds had
not seen me and I stayed there for several minutes with
my back and feet wedged on alternate sides of the
chimney listening to the chuckling noise the young eagles
were making. Williams put me down, and correctly so,
for not noting which peak it was that I had been climbing.

The rock climbing had been in 1954 immediately after
I got out of high school. My friend Sim, who was two
years older than I, was going to the architecture school

at the University of Michigan, where I was to start in
the fall. His project that year had been to design portable
minimum housing for migrant workers. He had come up
with a tent that was basically a modified geodesic dome.
The structural members were made of thin-wall aluminum electrical conduit with the ends hammered flat and
drilled and joined by quarter-inch bolts and wing nuts,
over which was stretched the canvas tent. The whole unit
weighed about fifty pounds and could be easily carried
on a car top. It took about twenty minutes to erect and
had an eight-foot-square floor space unobstructed by poles
in which a six-foot-tall man could stand up. The proto-
type had cost the university several hundred dollars, but
they figured that if mass-produced it could be made for
much less. They gave us the tent if we would write a re-
port after testing it for three months that summer under
varying conditions. We took it everywhere from Long
Island beaches to the top of Yosemite, which at that time
was only accessible by a six-hour drive over a twenty-mile-
long logging road. It was the first time I ever traveled
cross-country and I had a great time, but I doubt that any
fruit pickers ever benefited from it.

The most vivid memories that I have of that trip are
not at all about camping out but of the food on the road.
Most of the time it was the usual fare, Stuckey's for
Texaco gas and pralines or Colonel Sanders Finger-
Lickin' Good Fried Chicken. In one town in Indiana
the sign read "BROASTED CHICKEN," but at least
that sounded better than more fried. The inside of the
place looked like a polymer research laboratory. The employees all wore full-length white shop coats, the walls

were made of white-enameled steel panels, and the whole
place was dominated by a huge polished stainless steel
machine. There were temperature and pressure and
rate-of-flow gauges, and round hatches fitted with huge
locking wheels like the doors for the waterproof com-
partments in some John Wayne submarine movie. After
we placed our order for the only thing on the menu, the
attendant announced "two broasted chicken," took a few
paltry pieces of flesh that looked as though they had no
place next to all that stainless steel, and spun the wheel
with a flourish that opened up the bowels of the machine.
With an instrument that looked like an elongated surgeon's forceps (I have a natural aversion to forceps dating to the scar below my left eye inflicted by the doctor
who delivered me which causes a ptosis of that eye), the
attendant placed the raw chicken parts into the machine
and resealed it. Then he opened several gate valves and
started a stopwatch. After about one minute (I don't
wear a watch) he reversed the procedures and put before
us two orders of what I believe was once chicken. Broast-
ing turns out to be deep-fat frying in a histrionically ad-
ministered pressure cooker.

Terre Haute started to pick up neighborhood high-
rise trade plus some customers from downtown Max's,
but generally not the ones I would have preferred. There
were people like David, an academic poet who at best
will drink one glass of red pouring wine an evening,
whose life's work is an interminable didactic poem on
the contiguous relationships and probabilistic betting of
the stochastic chain theory of the origins of language. He
is now up to the section refuting the theory of language

diffusion as a function of epidemic (an idea that I never realized had been given much credence except by Artaud, and then only as an origin of European theatre) .

David is a good friend of Jackson MacLow, a chance poet who lives across the street from Poe Park in the Bronx and whom I have never seen in bars except to give readings. I have only seen the aurora borealis once, that when I was driving westward from N.Y.C. towards the Delaware Water Gap at 4:00 A.M. one September on my way to work. I had noticed an inordinate number of deer grazing along the side of the road for that time of year (the darker colored whitetails usually don't come down off the mountains until after the first snow has covered their ground browse) . The deer distracted me until I became aware that the sky was getting lighter in the west than it was in the east. As the ridge tops above the Water Gap became visible about twenty miles away, I saw the northern lights above them, extending into what appeared to be infinity. It looked like a returning ice age. Apparently the deer had been jacked out of the woods to the plain by the lights. Jackson often writes about the aurora borealis. His poems use all of the two-hundred-eighty types of available light as a permeating metaphor. It seems a fitting paradox that Jackson, who is the least conventional poet writing today, should consider Aristotle correct in the *Poetics* in claiming that sight is the primary sense at a time when less adventurous writers like Creeley reject the present need for such Aristotelian unities as beginning, middle and end. The choice of which of the two-hundred-eighty types of light he will use in any given poem is derived by the chance spelling of the dedicatee's

name. His poems are redeemed from gibberish, when
they are, by the stories which precede the light permutations (like the story of what he calls "The New England
Free Taxi Service"—a succession of suburban police cars
shuttling him from the town limits of one adjacent Massachusetts town to the next as he tried to hitchhike with
Billy Fare to Gloucester—occurring in a poem on the
death of Charles Olson). Last summer Jackson did some
work in California with a Dec PDP-9 computer (properly
termed a "programable film reader") using only forty-
eight character lines. He was trying to produce a series
of read-out poems from the permutations of fed-back
characters from a five-word line—something like a syste-
matic Molly Bloom orgasm. He couldn't understand why
the computer became self-canceling within the digital
retention system—the same effect he has been achieving
within the minds of his listeners for years.

Terre Haute also seemed to attract a lot of the minimal
artists who have for years lived off credit at Max's in exchange for their work. As much as I admire a return to
the barter system, I think Mickey is getting short shrift.
The ceilings at the new store are not very high and there
are wall sconces that break up the space so that there is no
room for large paintings. There are two DeSuvero drawings of arthritic hands that are as good as any Rembrandt
etching. The rest is a lot of clatfart. There are Flavin and
Zox drawings of larger works that are at Kansas City and
a Warhol self-portrait hung right at the entrance to the
john. The one piece that really interests me is by Frosty
Meyers. It consists of a Kulicke Lucite frame enclosing
the front page of the first run of the *Daily News* for

Monday, July 21, 1969, showing a two-thirds spherical
photograph of the moon with a tiny line drawing super-
imposed of the LM looking somewhat insect-like. It is
the same kind of unsophisticated drawings over photographs that the Hearst papers used to run seventy years
ago to provoke popular support of the Spanish-American
War or to describe lovers'-lane slayings. It is headed
"MAN LANDS ON THE MOON" and seems to have
been printed (with the exception of the two lead para-
graphs of text on page three, which give the time of
touchdown as 4:17:42 P.M. N.Y.C. time and quote the
final few seconds of conversation between Houston and
The Eagle) several hours before the actual landing. Evans
Webb, another frame maker, waited at the *Daily News*
offices for several hours and bought the first fifty copies of
the press run. He brought them down to Grand Street,
where a number of us, including Frosty, were watching
Wayne Timm's color television. Wayne is a painter who
makes his living as a bartender at Max's (his lifelong
ambition is to vend beer at Yankee Stadium for just one
day so that he can eighty-six some drunk). He used to
be a shipwright in Provincetown, but that is a disappearing trade, being replaced by fiber glassers. Franz Kline
used to have an old shipwright build his stretchers for
him—instead of the commonly used one-by-four clear
pine with quarter-inch plywood gusset plates screwed on
the back that most stretcher builders use, this man would
use two-by-two lumber with the same material for cross-
bracing, interlocking all the pieces with mortise and
tenon joints and turning the braces on a lathe so that they
resembled the leg patterns of a Colonial ladder-back

chair—of course none of this showed from the front.
Wayne takes photographs, mostly of athletes, from the
television set as models for his paintings. Just below the
encapsulated newspaper is what from any distance looks
like a thirty-five-millimeter black-and-white slide. It is
actually a piece of hard-fired ceramic on which has been
electrovacuum-plated a thin layer of tantalum, forming
the tracery of a drawing by Frosty of several minimal
geometric figures and a graffiti-like drawing of a cock
and balls. NASA made up these nearly indestructible
reproductions of drawings by Frosty, John Chamberlain,
Claes Oldenberg, and Andy Warhol and attached them
to a leg of the LM under the aluminum-foil heat shield.
They were abandoned on the moon floor with the descent
stage. It seems only fitting that the first art on the moon
should be considered obscene on the earth (and produced
by a man who would change his name from Forrest to
Frosty) and parallels the bored and fractious announcer
on Channel 7 with no hard-news to announce for hours
on end describing how the explorers would take Com-
munion wafers (there was no mention of any wine) and
then Seconal immediately after touching down.

Right after W. W. II, N.Y.C. changed over from
using heavy iron trash baskets on the street corners to
much lighter wire baskets. They soon started to disappear
at an unbelievable rate. Where they were all going became as common a topic of conversation at that time as
the speculation about flying saucers. The question was
finally answered by a cartoon in *The New Yorker*. It
showed a U.F.O. with two little antennate creatures
emerging unloading litter baskets labeled "Dept. Sanita-

tion," while in the sky could be seen a planet with the landmass outlines of North and South America. Channel 7 reported a few weeks ago that the baskets are still disappearing at the rate of 3,500 a year, over half of the sixty thousand baskets put out are missing. Current speculation is that people in the suburbs are stealing them to burn their leaves in. I've always tended to believe *New Yorker* cartoons—ever since they ran one during wartime gasoline rationing that showed an empty stretch of highway and two motorcycle cops hiding behind a billboard. One cop was saying to the other, "This time you play the speeder and I'll play the cop."

Frosty has been playing around with lasers for a couple of years. He installed one at Terre Haute which starts out in the back dining room and through a series of four mirrors ends up against the rear wall of the front dining room. It emits a pencil-thin beam of red light that runs parallel to and about six inches below the ceiling in a shape roughly approximating a square-cornered question mark. The beam of a laser can only be seen when looking towards its source and is invisible as receding light. People kept asking what it was for, to which I had no answer until one day Billy Brownrigg, one of the bartenders, told a curious customer that it showed the way back to the bathrooms, which it does. Billy is an ex-Marine, so Mickey hung on the back-bar wall a Malcolm Morley lithograph of a Marine flag bearer in full parade uniform standing before a triumphal arch. Most of the bar regulars are Billy's friends from Dr. Generosity, where he used to work, and he takes an awful lot of ribbing about that print—which should give some idea of

Mickey's sense of humor. But then any judgment of
Mickey's taste has always been a mystery to me. He insists
that half the selections on his jukebox, both at Kansas
City and at Terre Haute, be dreary narrative hill-billy
songs. I once replaced a couple of Merle Haggard songs
on the jukebox at Terre Haute with The Mamas and
The Papas' "Creque Alley" and Simon and Garfunkel's
"At the Zoo" (both of which have been out of print for
some time and took a lot of trouble to find) only to have
Mickey explain to me his poetic—he feels that the best
poetry tells a story and that today only country-and-
Western music follows in that tradition.

   Billy is an aspirant actor (as common among uptown
bartenders as painters are downtown) who spends his off
hours in other bars thinking up one-act plays. The one
he is working on now is called "The Last Supper"—in it
all the Apostles are on speed except Judas, who is stoned
on grass, which is why he is hungry. The dialogue sounds
like a cross between Lord Buckley's "The Naz" and the
usual sort of uptown-bar drug talk. I would doubt that
in a culture that sends Seconal to the moon that there is
any more drug use uptown than downtown, but in
uptown bars there is a lot more open uncool, ostenta-
tious talk. A great many of the cooks and dishwashers
in the bars on the strip are Chinese. They are the
real uptown heads. The bartenders claim that they
all drink *yen-chee-sui,* a drink made of mulled red
wine and opium ashes. There are sandbox bars where
people will sit for hours working out schemes to send
somebody's younger brother through pharmacy school
and then set him up in a drugstore in, say, Connecticut

just so as to have a source of supply. It doesn't seem to
matter that there are easier and cheaper and more expedient ways. There is often an edge of cruelty to uptown
stories. Sam O'Meara, another bartender at Terre Haute,
and Billy once told me about two sandbox regulars
who picked up two secretaries at a bar. They took the
girls to their place and partied all night. One of the girls
left to go to work in the morning and the other passed
out. The two guys took down the girl's pants, shaved her
pubic hair off (dry), and replaced the loose hair in her
underpants and redressed her. Then they waited for her
reaction when she woke up and went to piss.

When I had first taken the job at Max's uptown, Tony
Gould had said to me that the only thing that made the
hours (6:00 P.M. to 5:00 A.M.) bearable was drinking. In
the years that I have known him I have never seen him
drunk, so I thought his remark either callow or snide.
But I soon enough found that he was right. There were
so many interruptions to my drinking during the evening that I stopped drinking bourbon with ice and
changed to Cognac which wouldn't get diluted if I had
to leave it to settle an argument between waitresses or fix
the ice machine or whatever. I found myself, with the
exception of a girl about my own age named Susan,
thinking of waitresses as a total lot of misfits suffering from
delusions of adequacy. With the barrier of the customer-
waitress relationship that had been maintained at Kansas
City removed, all I could see was a bunch of twenty-one-
year-olds who took too many downs so as not to get hysterical over the provocations of solipsistic junior-executive
types out to prove to their dates how urbane they were.

Susan, who was the only girl at Terre Haute with previous waitress experience, had just separated from her husband (whom she always referred to only by his last name). She had the kind of mouth that has always turned me on, with the lip edges clearly defined without using makeup (Desmond Morris speaks of this demarcation of the lip margins as one of the prime signals of the heightened sexuality of humans over other primates). She had formerly worked in a discotheque and she taught the other waitresses at Terre Haute all the tricks she had learned there—like bringing a customer his change on a wet cork-covered serving tray so that the coins and bills stuck to the tray. That way the customer either had to lose his cool prying each piece loose, or more likely he would just leave a bigger tip. I found that no matter how much I drank, at the end of the night I was still clear-headed and never had trouble clearing the registers or adding the receipts. I came to welcome any change in the routine. Three years ago there had been a holdup of the night receipts from the Academy of Music movie theatre when the manager was making the night drop at the bank (which happens to be the same bank that Kansas City uses). Tony was headed for the bank with his final drop when he saw a man handcuffed to the door handles of the bank and the cops all around. He assumed that there had been an attempted holdup and that the cops had arrested the man. They told him he couldn't use the night deposit box and explained what had happened. Before the movie manager got to the bank, two men had blown sand from a syringe into the night-deposit box lock cylinder, jamming it. Then they waited in the doorway and when the manager had his back turned to them trying to force his key into the lock, they approached him from behind, held him up, and handcuffed him to the door handles. The one time I found the night-deposit box near Terre Haute stuck, I thought it might be a setup (there are four bars that all make their 4:00-A.M. drops at that bank). I took the receipts plus all the money in the safe and brought it to Max's downtown. It was one of the few times that the tedium up there was broken. The next day the bank called to explain that a supermarket had put in a shopping bag containing its deposit and the looped-twine carrying handles had jammed in the mechanism. Bank night-deposit boxes have fascinated me ever since I read several years ago of an employee at a bank in Pittsfield, Massachusetts, who put a dummy night-deposit box outside the bank at night not connected to the chute to the vault. He got away with over sixty thousand dollars.

Anyway, I routinely drank my Cognac and got bored. I would watch the liquid climb up the inside of the glass, form into droplets, and then roll back down to the level of the edge of the meniscus. The action, which never ceases, is caused by the increase in surface tension as the more volatile alchohol evaporates from the thin film of Cognac on the inside of the glass, thus drawing up more Cognac from below until the weight of the drop overcomes its film strength and it rolls down. C. V. Boys in his excellent series of science lectures for children in 1890, with typical nineteenth-century scholarly skepticism, explained the passage in Proverbs, "Look not thou upon the wine when it is red, when it giveth his colour in the cup, when it moveth itself aright," as a warning against fortified wines, and went on to urge his teenage audience to consider that all such Biblical passages that did not seem to make sense must also refer to what was then common knowledge but has since been forgotten.

I found I didn't have time to read newspapers anymore or to sit with Sam in Ratner's late at night after Max's had closed dreaming up ever more absurd sex scenes for his dirty books (e.g., Ratner's serves so many thousands of rolls every day that they must use the sidewalk vaults to store them in—why not an orgy scene of waitresses and drinkers from Max's on top of this mountain of onion rolls beneath the sidewalks at 4:30 A.M. counterpointed against the awakening city and respectable customers eating in the restaurant). I think the reason Sam writes only pornography (besides the obvious money) is that it is the one form in which the author's imagination is allowed complete freedom.

The only source of news I had was radio or occasionally television, and they never draw the parallel connections that give any meaning to raw news (Angelo Dundee, explaining his criterion for refusing to allow Jimmy Ellis to reenter the ring against Frazier, said that his test of a fighter's consciousness is to drop ice cubes down the front of his trunks and see if he winces—this is essentially the same test devised by transplant specialists to determine brain death in a heart donor, the doctors pour ice water into the dying person's ear and watch to see if this causes the eye pupils to contract). Even when I got to read the *Times,* it didn't seem the same. On the twenty-fifth anniversary of the bombing of Dresden the *Times*

ran stories for two days. Neither story even bothered to
mention that the intensity of the bombing had created a
fire storm, much less explain how this new phenomenon
made the resulting fire self-stoking and almost impossible
to combat. There doesn't seem to be any more journalism
like Leibling spending years trying to isolate a particular
taste remembered from bouillabaisse in Europe and
finally discovering a discarded fish that he was totally unfamiliar with in a wholesale market in New Jersey and
being told that it was poisonous. It turns out that the
very best-tasting bouillabaisse must contain the toxic ke-
tone rotenone in very small quantities. Or Berton
Rouche's piece in *The New Yorker* some years ago that
ranks with the best forensic medical investigation, tracing
an outbreak of trichinosis in N.Y.C. While Leibling was
alive, he functioned as a conscience to all newspapers; and
the *Times,* as the closest thing we have to a national record, was a great newspaper. It seems a particular over-
sight after Vonnegut's novel not to mention the fire
storm, but it is just characteristic of present-day report-
age. As just one example of the changes over the last ten
years—when the Wanamaker Building suffered a severe
fire about twelve years ago the *Times* not only had good
coverage of the fire but in a backup article mentioned
that in the fire chief's examination in, if I remember correctly, 1911 one of the questions had been to outline the
strategy necessary to combat a major fire in just that
building, a fact that reveals more about the nature of
urban fire control than any amount of descriptive prose.
But then we have turned into a nation of sutlers. Eric's
wife dates this change in national purpose to the gift of

the evil spirit dwelling in the Hope diamond to the
Smithsonian by Harry Winston at just about the same
time. The closest the *Times* can come now to good writing is when it parodies itself (e.g., in a book review,
without a by-line, of Sugar Ray Robinson's autobiography which was ghost-written by *Times* sportswriter Dave
Anderson, "Walker Smith, Jr. was born . . . in Detroit in
1921. . . . He boxed in his first amateur match . . . in 1936.
His coach identified him with an Amateur Athletic Union
card that belonged to one Ray Robinson. The name
stuck, along with the nickname Sugar, which was offered
by a woman who thought his style sweet." No shit) .

I found myself partially remembering lists and mne-
monic devices. For some reason about the fifth grade I was
forced to memorize by rote the list of auxiliary verbs
(beisamarewaswerebeingbeen, couldwouldshould, may-
canmustmighthashadhave, dodoesdid) , to this day I
haven't the slightest notion what for. All I recall was
"King Phillip came over from Germany . . ." for king-
dom, phylum, class, order, family, genus, species, and
variety, I couldn't remember what the end of the device
was for species and variety, but I could remember black,
brown, red, orange, yellow, green, blue, violet, gray and
white (the standard color-coding bands used on electronic
resistors and capacitors to designate impedance ratings) ,
but all I retained of the memory device was "Bad boys
rape only young girls. . . ." I started remembering isolated
facts out of my life that had to do with my conception
of good and bad (I haven't been able to think in terms
of evil since LeRoi wrote that poem saying that "love"
spelled backwards is "evil") . When I had been working

on the farm we used to catch snapping turtles and put
them in fifty-five-gallon drums filled with sour milk and
corn meal. There would be a lattice of boards on the
bottom so that shit would settle below and so that they
could get their heads up by stretching so as to be able to
breathe. In two years of this forced feeding they would
grow to about fifty pounds and make great eating. This
kind of cruelty towards animals seems fairly prevalent
among farmers, as with the Strasbourg geese whose feet
are nailed through the webbing to the floor (so that they
can't dissipate their energy in nonproductive exercise)
and then they have corn forced down their throats by a
crank-fed funnel-like device that works on the same
principles as an automatic coal stoker. Their livers become enormously enlarged and they make the very best
pâté.

There is always present in a bar the possibility of incipi-
ent violence. I had never given it much thought at Max's
(there are bars like the Chit-Chat where it is dangerous
ever to forget it) except to avoid those creeps who will
provoke a fight just to get beaten up. But I found that
the only times that there was trouble at Terre Haute was
when I was off the floor doing an inventory in the basement
or the like. Mickey has never used a bouncer on the door,
figuring correctly that if you have a heavy it gives an excuse to anybody who is feeling belligerent. On busy
nights at Kansas City he has a four-foot eleven-inch-tall
girl name Ronnie work the door to exclude nonregulars
who might cause trouble, she just tells them "dinner
only." Nobody yet has taken a poke at her, most guys
looking for a fight don't want to start in with an eighty-

seven-pound girl. I can't accept the notion that "vibrations" is an adequate answer to why fights don't start when I'm around, but there has to be some presence felt. Diane says I scowl a lot. The way I got my O.E.D. was by acting as a bodyguard for a girl I knew from school who was in the midst of an involved divorce action that was finally settled for several hundred thousand dollars. (She grew up in Queens on roller derbies, but now that she is a rich woman and hip to all that is current, she plans to use some of her money to sponsor a different type of confrontation. She plans to endow an annual competition pitting teams of groupies and women's-lib chicks in an enclosed arena to see who, if any, would emerge). Her husband was a somewhat unstable man who once punched out her older brother and her father during a visit with their infant son and she was justifiably worried. I'm not sure just why she chose me to protect her and her son except that she knew I wanted to get the dictionary and that I probably would have refused a gift that I didn't work for.

Anyway, her husband didn't cause any trouble at all the two times he visited, and then he stopped coming around on his appointed days. All I had to do was read the *Times*, holding it low enough so that I could peer over the top edge of the sheet keeping an eye him while he awkwardly played with his son on the floor for one hour a week. The January 11, 1968, *Times* (London) *Literary Supplement* had an article by Marghanita Laski explaining how Oxford University Press goes about gathering data for a proposed revised edition. The primary difference between the O.E.D. and any other dictionary is that it gives

citations for the first usage of every word, along with citations for every denotative and connotative change, and
also cites the last known usage of obsolete words (e.g.,
the first usage of the word "sex" to mean more than the
forms of division between male and female is cited from
Donne's "The Primrose," "For should my true-Love lesse
then woman bee,/She were scarce any thing; and then,
should she/ Be more then woman, shee would get above/
All thought of sexe, and thinke to move/ My heart to
study her, and not to love") . Most changes are wrought,
as would be expected, by poets, the way Ed Sanders has in
the course of the last ten years totally changed the common
usage of the word "freak." It seems totally fitting to me
that the only omission that I have been able to find in
the O.E.D. that isn't either a post-publication neologism
or connotative change, is the word combination "grain-
thief," which I found in a Jack Daniel's ad. It is a tool
consisting of a hollow tube about three feet long with
oval holes cut along its length. It is plunged into a grain
bin in order to take core samples so as to determine if
all the grain is of equal quality to that which is visible
at the top. I told Julie about my word and he said he had
also seen the word "thief" used in a Carolina Biological
Supply Company catalog to denote a device that consisted
of a bottle on the end of a cord for taking lake-water
samples, with a mechanism so that it can be uncorked by
manipulation from the surface and then a sample re-
trieved from the depth that is desired. It is used by ich-
thyologists.

   Once on my night off I was up at Terre Haute when
Steve Taylor came in, back from the house in the Thou-

sand Islands where he goes whenever he has saved enough
from carpentry work. He was broke so I bought him
dinner and then we sat at the bar drinking beer while he
went into a trancelike monologue about the time he had
spent in Morocco in the Peace Corps. He had been living
alone for months without speaking to anybody and his
voice cracked like a record I once heard of monks who
had taken vows of silence singing a High Mass:

I was staying with Lance up in Buderbella, this little town
up in the foothills of the Atlas Mountains, Berber and Arab
country both, at the C.T. [*centre du travaux*], which was the
agricultural work station that we were working at, everybody
there was studying agriculture except for the *shoushs* and the
jeep drivers. A *shoush* is a messenger boy, actually it's a made-
up job. One guy down in Settat, his job was to turn the lights
on in the evening and off in the morning, just a created job,
the same thing that's going to have to happen here. He made
two hundred dirhans a month, five dirhans to the dollar, that's
forty dollars, right? My old man makes that in an hour and
a half. He gets his house free, it just pays for his food. Buderbella was a great place, where we were staying, it had horses,
and cows and bulls. Si Ali was *shoush* who took care of the
animals, he was also a Koranic teacher, a *faqi* in Arabic, which
means he knew ancient Arabic and taught lessons. The C.T.
came and wiped out that whole village, they built it right
on the top of this little village, it was an abandoned *duar*, that's
a village, even if it's just a man and his wife and two kids that's
a *duar*. He was a saint. He used to heal people by writing
things from the Koran on a piece of paper and then tell them
what to do with it. One day a woman came to him and said
that her husband was going to divorce her because she couldn't
give him any children. So he wrote something from the Koran

on a piece of paper with his own ink, he brewed it, and said, "Wash this off in your husband's soup." She went home and did it and she was pregnant a month later. He got fired from the C.T., he was a white Berber, from way up in the mountains, just as white as a sheet, much whiter than I am. He had blue eyes. I asked him where he was from, he said way way away, nobody's ever been there, it takes three days to ride there. Lance hired him for a houseboy, he taught Lance classical Arabic. They expected you to have a servant. Anyway, while I was staying there we were stoned the whole time. They had a couple of riding horses. I was still in the Peace Corps, but I was on my way out. Lance was still in, his job was painting signs. They were picture signs for the farmers, to try to show them that fertilizer was good. Like it would show a very simple thing, a picture of a bag of fertilizer, and then below it would show Arab men fertilizing the soil, and then a picture of a good wheat crop. Then the picture below that would show the lazy Moroccan smoking hashish and no wheat. So he told me to go riding, and he told me where to go, to go down this road and then up this way, and you'll come out into the springtime. I went riding down this road and came to the other road, and they were building an irrigation ditch all the way up the road. I was saying hello to everyone I saw anywhere, to be the first one to say hello. They, none of them said hello, they just looked and went back to work. I couldn't understand it, but in a way I figured it out, that was that I was a European on horseback. That is the biggest put-down of them all, because they want cars, and here comes a European riding a horse and they think that that's the lowest means of travel. It really freaked them out, it was worse than walking. I kept on riding, I went up way past them up to these fields. Fields covered with poppies and mustard flowers and different orange-, red- and lilac-colored thistles. While I was up there, I got stoned, I took a big

joint up there with me, and so I slid off the horse just to stretch
my legs, and I picked up all these flowers off the hillside, stuck
them in the bridle and the saddle, stuck them in my hair, stuck
them up in the horse's nose, all over, man, everyplace I could
find I stuck flowers, different colors. I was riding back down
about an hour later and said hello to the workers, and they
looked up and started laughing, and they said, "Hi," and
started talking to each other and laughing and asked how I
was. They knew I didn't believe those signs about fertilizer and
hashish. Once they asked me how they do it in America. I said
they do it with airplanes. I just answered their question.

The first *duar* I went to blew my mind, way out in the hillside, we drove up in a jeep over the hill and all the kids came
out to greet us. That's all I saw the first time. I just couldn't
believe it, I kept waiting for Jesus, it looked like it could have
been two thousand years ago. And all these Arabs were arguing
with each other, we were handing out sickles and trying to
record their names. I couldn't understand a word. There was
no such thing as a line, they kept crowding around. After a half
hour we gave up and had lunch there for two or three hours,
and then we drove away. We'd do about half an hour's work a
day. The government made the farmers buy fertilizer, even if
they didn't want it, they would force them to buy it, it was
potassium fertilizer, I think sulfates and phosphates, they have
one of the world's largest supplies of potassium, it comes from
the southern half of the country north of the mountains, north
of Marrakesh inside the Atlas Mountains, the southern plains,
it's almost like desert. A couple of the farmers resold it to the
big landowners. They threw them in jail. It makes the plants
grow tall for a couple of years and then it burns out the soil and
then the wheat grows stunted. It fucks up the earth. They threw
a friend of mine in jail for drinking, it's illegal. He wasn't hurt-
ing anybody. They throw you in jail there for drinking. It's

illegal for a Muslim to drink alcohol or smoke kif, but they
don't care much about the kif, just like we don't care about the
alcohol. They asked me if there was kif in America. I said sure
there was, but not as much. They asked how much it was. I
told them that in New York it was twenty-five dollars an ounce.
They showed me how much they had and I said that would be
ten dollars. Man, every one of them wanted to go into business. What they had cost them about twenty cents. Their kif is
mixed with tobacco, but it's all cleaned. They say it is very bad
to smoke without tobacco, how much tobacco you put in is up
to you. It's good grass, but they smoke it all day long, never
once did I get too high there. Everybody's stoned. Everybody's
walking down the street so slow and they're bumping into each
other. The first time I walked in the street I was straight and
my eyes were just popping out of my head, and my nose, first
time I really knew what it was like to smell, everything here's
covered up, but there I smelled shit in the street, I smelled fresh
fruit in the stands, fresh meat, and *oud,* that fantastic incense.
When I first got there I wouldn't walk into the *medina,* the
old city, at night, but now I can walk down any street in the
whole country any hour of any day, and not fear. Nothing's
going to happen to you, there aren't as many crazy people as
here.

Did I tell you about the head beating? It all started one
morning Ron and I got up, it was in Settat, Ron and I got up
and smoked our morning pipe or two, and were walking down
the street on the way to have our coffee, the usual procedure. It
was Saturday morning, *souk* day, that means market day in the
town. Right up behind Ron's house was the market, and this
place has the largest weekly camel market in Morocco, it's the
largest town between Casablanca and Marrakesh, it's a truck
stop, it has forty-two cafés and they're open all night. There are
more freaks in that town than I've seen anywhere else, butch-

ers, crazy butchers. What happened that morning, there's one butcher called El Hej, *hej* is somebody who's been to Mecca, the first time I'd met him we were in Mustefa's café, Ron had told me about him that he was drunk and always stoned, never changes his clothes, and walks around with the sharpest knife in town. They call him El Hej, but he hasn't been to Mecca, it's like saying "sir." The first time I met him he came in and he was drunk, and so Ron introduced him to me, and he started kissing Ron, and he started kissing me, his spit was running down my neck, and man, he had that fucking knife, and I was just sitting there lapping it up, I was the nicest guy he ever met, he had reason to kiss me like that. Anyway, we got up that morning to have coffee and we're walking down the street, and we saw four horses underneath these pepper trees. There was one horse, a gold horse that was being held by a man in the middle of four pepper trees, they were evenly planted, just prancing around in circles, up and down, up and down, just frothing at the mouth, and this guy just hanging on for dear life. The most beautiful horse I've ever seen, and when the sunlight through the tree hit it, it glittered, long beautiful stallion, it had a honey-colored mane and honey-colored tail, and it hung down to the ground, it was just, just dancing, just dancing, up and down. So we decided to stay the coffee and go up to the *souk* and look at the animals, we almost bought a camel that day, we were asking the price of this white camel, it was two hundred dirhans, that's fifty dollars, it was a young camel. Camels are something else, they all look like Bette Davis, every goddamned camel in the world looks like Bette Davis at her most conceited, at her most indignant, they just look at you. You walk up there and you look at it, and you say, "Hi, camel," he looks at you, bored stiff, and he'll look at you and you walk by and he'll follow you with his eyes, and when you stand there for a while and look at him, he'll turn his head, just like that, nose up, and look away and fart. Fantastic animals, nobody's friend. They're like goats, they've got real character. We turned down to the butcher's and he saw us, and remember this butcher's nuts, he saw us and said, "Wait a minute," this butcher's nuts, he's twenty-one years old and he's been smoking since he was ten, this isn't El Hej, it's another guy, he doesn't have his own stall in the butcher market, he doesn't even have his own knives, he borrows knives. He just perched up a little wooden table at the end of all the rows of butcher shops, right at the end, the first one you see, he's got his meat there and he's borrowing knives from the butchers behind him. He saw us coming and he came running down the steps and we lit up a pipe, he gave us his pipe, and he said, "I'll be right back," and he gave us his pipe and his kif to hold, so we had a couple of pipes and he was gone about forty-five minutes, we didn't know where he was, and he came back with this tray with tea and glasses, sat down and drank tea and had a few more pipes together, and then he walked us all the way around the *souk,* and we were walking back down the road to have coffee again, and we saw this gold horse again. Except this time it had been saddled, it had a lilac and gold saddle on it and a rider with a miquelet-lock musket in his left hand, he was a dark Arab dressed in a white *jaloba,* in all white, and he was pulling the reins in. Before the horse had been perfectly free, he had no trappings on him, and all of his muscles were going, the next time I saw him, uptight, like all that power had been contained. There were seven horses altogether, and seven riders, some in black, all beautifully different. They started riding down the street, with a man playing a *grita,* that's a flute with a disk that you put your lips right up to and stick the double reed right in your mouth and puff your cheeks out like bags, and then you blow. It's a wooden horn with bells on the bottom, it's named after the *grita* flower that makes you high.

And so he, this kid that was playing, he was about twenty years old, he had learned how to breathe in through his nose while blowing out through his mouth, so that his music was ceaseless, he didn't have to stop and take a breath, just pouring music out, just rippling notes. Just going down the street and these four horses were in front of him all with muskets and this crowd of people behind him, and there was a belly dancer with him, a male belly dancer, you never see a woman dance in public, except in a bar in Casablanca or Tangiers. He wasn't really a belly dancer, he was just a freak, the guy was like he had a rod up his ass when he started dancing. The women were hooting. Did you see *The Battle of Algiers*? That sound, it's almost like a yodel, quavering, fluttering sound the women make it in the back of their throats, actually they do that when they send a man off to battle, it's not a lament, it's a sort of a victory cry, it's what haunted the French in Algiers coming out of the *medina* every night. The Algerians are a young people, they're the only ones who can get it together, they're like the Israelis. Two Egyptians couldn't carry either end of a board together without trying to go through the door at the same time. We saw this horse and we got in right behind them, they got up to the *souk* and the camels were coming out of the *souk* and going into the *souk* at the same time, and donkeys and burros and mules, and these horses were freaked out by the camels, and they started moving sideways and backwards into the crowd, and the music freaked them out and the women hooting, it was the highest situation I've ever seen, the most ecstatic. These horses were just going crazy, a sea of people, and the horses were just like ships. They got by the camels, and the dancer got the urge, he ran out in front of the musician and started dancing and the horses formed a semicircle on the other side from the crowd, and the women were saying, "*Affrit, affrit,*" that is "Possessed, possessed," and he was, he was just a blur. At the end of the dance he would jump up and spook one of the horses, just hit it in the nose, the horse would rear up and all of the men would shoot off their muskets. Then the horses would turn around and the music would keep on playing, the men would hand their muskets to their boys on the ground for reloading, and they'd ride on up the street. Over and over, they went all the way around town, they stopped maybe six or seven times. They ended up at the house of this man called Sheik el Bashir, he's a holy man, he's the leader of this fraternity, it's called a *zouia*. We asked somebody what was going on, all we got out of it was that it was going to be a head-beating contest, and that it was a weird sect, like the *Penitentes* out in New Mexico, that they were ashamed of, because it was pagan. They slaughtered two bull calves. The Sheik lives in a house attached to the tombs of his father and his grandfather, that's a *zouia*, a fraternity formed around the tomb and the house of a saint. This man's father and his grandfather were saints, they kept giving food to the poor, but when he was young and his father was living, he ran off to Rabat and Casablanca and fucked whores and drank. His father died and he came right back and lived in this house, and never comes out except at night to give away food. We thought in respect we should leave. The next Saturday was Mohammed's birthday and we went to Marrakesh, but it was not a public celebration. The Saturday following, two weeks after the horses, we heard this music coming from in front of the Sheik's house and we went up there and there were seven of these *affritas* dancing, and a bunch of drummers, and a whole crowd of people. They were exhausted, they had been dancing all night and they had had nothing to eat and nothing to drink. A couple of their wives were dancing along with them to support them, one wife started to freak out and pull off her clothes, and they hauled her away. The man who was running it was swinging a huge burner of incense at the crowd to keep them back, and Sheik el Bashir was standing in the doorway white as a ghost, he had seen no sunshine, dressed in white including he had a white cloth wrapped around his chin and part of his face. In turns the dancers would go up and bow down to the Sheik's feet and ask for something and be refused. Then a man brought out a kettle full of water and spilled it in the mud, and one of the dancers dove in head first and came up laughing hysterically, and then would dive in again and come up crying and calling out, *"Ah-luh, Ah-luh,"* over and over, laughing and then crying, and pointing at everything he saw. After a while he stopped and they all started dancing again, and every half hour or so someone would ask the Sheik for something, and he would shake his head no. Finally the man who brought out the kettle went back in and came out with this chain about four feet long with big handwrought links and a solid wooden ball about twenty-six inches around at its end. He handed it to the first man, who took it in both hands and started swinging it out in front of him and ram it with his head, and then he'd swing it out in front of him again and ram it with his head again, they had all shaven their heads before the rite. After a while the guy who had been burning incense would take it from him and give it to another dancer, and he'd do the same thing, there were only seven of them, once upon a time there were maybe a hundred of them. All the dancers did this, but they kept going up to the Sheik still, for another half an hour, finally the man went into the house again and came out with a double-bitted Cretan axe and gave it to the first dancer, who started jumping up and down, up and down in a one-two rhythm, and then he'd go wham, and hit himself on the head with the axe, they bled a lot, but I don't know why they didn't bust their heads wide open, that's what blew my mind. It's a *sufi*, that is mystical, rite like the dervishes levitating. There's one in Turkey, which is much more pagan, where

they draw a circle in the dirt around any man in the sect who is
evil, and he can't get out. The *hamedsha,* that's the sect that I
saw in Morocco, believe in direct communication with God,
just me and the man, and they believe that God won't let them
die, *hamedsha* comes from the same root word for "Mohammed." What happened was that they were just bleeding all over
the place, and the man with the incense took the axe from them
after they had each beaten themselves with it three or four
times, and the man came to the first one and squeezed a lemon
into the cuts to make it stop bleeding and wrapped his head in
a turban, and then each dancer did that for the next. One of
the men looked like he was eighty years old. When each one
finished they were absolutely sober, it was unreal, as though
nothing had happened, it was like any other day, they didn't
talk, nobody came near them, those men were to be left in
peace, they didn't even look exhausted. The next day I was
wandering around town and one of them was a butcher, one of
them, the old man, he was a street sweeper, everyday people.
A friend of mine saw a *sufi* rite down in Safi, down near the
coast, where they ate prickly-pear cactus fruit, can you imagine
that?

Steve and I had done a couple of jobs together,
mostly photographers' studios. He was the first person to
turn me on the Um Kalthoum, the Egyptian singer, we
used to go out to Atlantic Avenue in Brooklyn to buy
her records. She looks like Kate Smith, but she is *affrit.*
Steve went to Expo 67 in Montreal and got talking in
Arabic to a man working at the Israeli pavilion. He asked
if they listened to Um Kalthoum in Israel. The man said
of course (Radio Cairo plays two hours of her music
every night). Later Steve asked the man if Israel had the
atomic bomb, the man said yes, but that they wouldn't

drop it until after Um Kalthoum died of old age. She
was Farouk's darling and he gave her many jewels and an
island in the Nile where she lives with her husband, who
is a doctor. She has her own mosque, and five times a day
she goes up to the minaret and calls herself to prayer.
When Nasser took over, a journalist for a Cairo newspaper, in order to gain the favor of the new regime, wrote
that anybody who loved her was a hash-head. Nasser was
so enraged that he forced a retraction, and then had the
man fired. She is now sixty-eight and has been the most
famous singer in the Arab world for fifty years. She sings
in public only on the third Thursday of each month. Her
songs are all repetitive short lyric love poems, what she
does with them is like listening to John Coltrane play for
forty-five minutes before you realize that he has been
playing variations on the melody of "These Are a Few of
My Favorite Things." (For centuries it had been thought
that the earliest lyrics in a vulgar European language
were by Guillaume de Poitiers, sometimes spelled Guillem
de Peitau, who lived in Provence from 1071 to 1127. In
1948 research into a form of Arabic lyric poem from
Spain called *muwashshahas,* dated to the early eleventh
century, revealed that the final stanzas of this rigid form
called for a four-line verse, called a *jarcha,* to be written
not in classical Arabic but in a vulgar tongue. Some
jarchas were written in Hebrew, but most were done in
Spanish. They all took the form of a maiden's lament.
The songs that Um Kalthoum sings follow directly in the
tradition of these Mozarabic songs. Although she will sing
a song of several hours' duration, there are only three or
four lines of verse, of a love-sick woman's lament, typical

is *"At Lal,"* meaning "the ruins," or more specifically the
ashes of an abandoned Bedouin campfire.)

Steve grew up in Ohio, but his family comes from West
Virginia. He once went to visit his grandmother there.
Steve has very long hair and a droopy mustache and he
thought that his hill-billy relatives would give him a hard
time, but his grandmother told him that he looked just
like her father. My family has never been very close, I
have cousins who live in N.Y.C. who I've never met.
My mother's parents were the only people I really liked
when I was a boy. My father's father died when I was two,
but I remember his mother. She was getting senile and
came to live with us for a year when I was seven. I had
heard that she had false teeth, I didn't know what that
meant, but I didn't like her because of it. She never threw
anything out and there were crumbling cardboard boxes
in the attic full of her things. I used to rummage through
them trying to figure out who she was. I found a pair of
red lobster claws in one of the boxes and thought that
they were her false teeth (I had never seen a lobster).
After that I wouldn't stay in the same room with her and
must have made that poor old woman's life miserable. I
imagined what she must have looked like when she put
in her red false teeth, and understood why she hid them
in the attic. It wasn't until several years later that I found
out what a lobster was and realized that those were not
her teeth, and it wasn't until even more years later that I
realized that, since it was violation of the Kosher dietary
laws for her to have eaten a lobster, that that was why she
had hidden them, but by the time I recognized her hu-
manity and defiance she had long since died.

Often the people who came into Terre Haute that I could talk to were not there to talk, they came there because it was less crowded than Kansas City. David Budd would sometimes come in with William Burroughs for a business conference and use the back room. David is a painter who is doing a movie about Arthur Flegenheimer (Dutch Schultz), for which Burroughs is writing the script. David has as much 1930's underworld arcane trivia in his head as Donald Phelps has about comic strips. He is always talking about people like Pistol Pete, who was the most successful dinger in N.Y.C. (a dinger is a man who pins little flags on the lapels of passing strangers and cons them out of a dollar—making them think it has something to do with veterans). He is the only person I have ever heard use the word "toney," he does it as though it were common speech. I have never seen it in print except in the *Daily News,* which uses it to mean "fancy or elegantly stylish people"—but then David lives in the disappearing post-Damon Runyon world of tabloid reality.

Terre Haute became a place of one-liners, rather than lovingly told stories. Mario Yrisarry, one of the first painters in N.Y.C. to use a spray gun, would walk in, take one look at the new waitress and say, "I didn't think anything was that beautiful except my paintings," or some regular from downtown would walk in and say, "So this is Max's Schrafft's." I suppose Mickey invites this sort of thing, as he speaks that way himself. He'll say (about a workman more concerned with getting paid than with the quality of his work), "My electrician is a taximeter," but he also will call the best service bartender he ever had work for him "a mechanic."

With all the enforced idleness of the job as bar manager, just the type of idleness I used to avoid when I was
a shop foreman, I found myself trying to recapitulate
previously read arguments from books and try to apply
them more broadly—I have always tended to apply the
specific to the general. Kenneth Slack, in his book about
Slocum's sloop, the *Spray,* tries to counter the derogation
of many yachtsmen for a boat which started life as an
oysterman. Slack makes the point that the progression of
modern sail marine architecture has increasingly been
towards boats that handle well in tight spaces at the expense of increased leeward slip. The *Spray,* with interior
cast-cement ballast (rather than the modern practice of
lead weighting at the bottom of the keel), was excellent
off the wind and was never designed to be run close-
hauled. When Slocum rebuilt her, he had in mind circum-
navigating the world, running before the prevailing
trades, not the tacking expected of a sports yacht. This
same increasing specificity of modern design is, in my own
experience, most apparent in motorcycles. When I used to
race them (in the 250cc class), I traveled to road-racing
tracks with my friend Tony Woodman, who was the best
lightweight road racer this country has yet produced.
Most racing in this country is on oval dirt tracks, but this
was in the early 1960s when European-style racing on
twisting pavement courses was just starting here. Once
up at Laconia, New Hampshire, after the race (which
Tony won), two spectators offered to let us try out their
new Greeves trials machines. A trials is an endurance run,
over rocks, downed trees, across streams, &c. where the
object is not speed but the maintenance of a perfect bal-

ance; points are subtracted for touching your foot to the
ground (indicating a loss of balance). The maximum
speed of a trials machine is about thirty miles per hour.
The engine of my TD-1 Yamaha would stall at that speed
even in the bottom gear of its five-speed box unless I
slipped the clutch. We took the Greeves into the woods
that form the infield of the old course at Laconia, where
I promptly fell into a ditch, the near vertical walls of
which came up to my shoulders. After one trial run in
which I stalled the engine, I found that these goatlike
machines were designed to be ridden out of just such a
situation. It had never occurred to me that there could
be so much exhilaration in riding a machine slowly.
Neither machine would have been suitable or for that
matter even usable on the public roads; like my Doberman bitch, they had been engineered for one specialty.

They are like the square gray polyurethane plastic
wastebasket at the Guggenheim Museum. It is used to
catch the drippings from the spigot of the coffee urn in
the museum lobby during intermission at their weekly
series of poetry readings. Neatly stenciled in two-and-a-
half-inch block letters on each of the four sides is
"POETRY."

I began to understand why all the foremen I had ever
worked for had been such pricks. When I became a foreman, I had paid my mechanics better than the going
wage, figuring that Henry Ford (despite all of his later
vicious anti-unionism) had been right when he established a higher daily wage (five dollars a day for everyone) than at that time prevailed, on the grounds that it
paid off if (in the example he used to give) a janitor

would bother to pick a discarded wrench up off the floor
and replace it where it belonged rather than just sweep
it out. There may be certain ego-trip satisfactions for the
owner of a bar if that's the way he gets his kicks. Bruce
claims that one Friday night when there was a line
formed outside of St. Adrians waiting to get in, a limousine pulled up and six people got out. Bruce was working
the door and one of the men from the car came up to
him and said that it was Huntington Hartford's party and
could they come in. Bruce, who is very slightly built, told
them that he had worked for years for Hartford for a
dollar an hour and that now he could damn well wait in
line. They did. A shop foreman (which is basically what
a bar manager is) who doesn't have any real work ends
up with nothing else to do but excoriate the people who
work for him. That's bad enough in a garage, but I'd be
damned if I was going to work at a job where I had to
do it to waitresses.

I gave Mickey notice after working at Terre Haute for
four months. He wasn't a bad boss, but the hours of rec-
ollection rather than accomplishment led to a dreariness
that I could see no point in perpetuating. About two
weeks before the new manager was scheduled to replace
me, a picture editor at *Look* magazine called up and said
she would like to use Terre Haute as the backdrop for
several pictures in a photo essay they were doing on new
styles to be called "Ban the Bra." It was arranged for the
photographers and models to come in the early afternoon
before the dinner rush. I came to work early the second
day of shooting to see how it was going. The photographer was having problems with the flat-chested model

getting visible nipple definition even through her cling-
ing dress. He suggested that she stand outside for a minute to chill them. Then he got the bartender to give her
ice cubes and sent her into the other room to rub the ice
on her nipples to try to make them erect. None of this
made any visible difference. It never seemed to occur to
any of them that there are other ways of arousing a
woman than the application of cold. Finally the model
got an idea—she took two shriveled dried chick peas from
a bowl on top of the bar (they serve the same thirst-
inducing function at Mickey's two bars that pretzels do at
most bars) and placed them under her dress in lieu of
nipples. The photographer got the effect he wanted and
the picture-taking session was quickly completed. (It
seemed to make about as much sense as the television
panel program immediately following the assassination of
Robert Kennedy, on which all the participants were ad-
vocating gun control, the program was sponsored by an
insurance company, each commercial opened with a picture of the corporate logo—a Minute Man armed with a
flintlock rifle. Or the indoor flagstaff at the 1968 Chicago
convention which was fitted with slits through which compressed air was pumped so as to make the flag flutter out
erect.)

ROCK CLIMBING
IN IRA, VERMONT

THERE ARE FEW visible rocks in western Vermont.
Called the Green Mountain State, to the casual observer
the name is more or less accurate, unless the underbrush
is penetrated. There are, of course, some outcroppings of
the continental rock itself, plus the annual crop of small
boulders appearing each spring on the cleared land by
frost heave, and the stones, boulders and bedrock exposed
by streams. There is nothing in central Vermont like the
rocks further south and west in the Appalachians. Driving
west into New York State or east into New Hampshire,
it becomes quite apparent that the boundaries of Vermont are at least as much geographic as they are political.

Eight miles southwest of Rutland, between the Clarendon River and Ira Brook, in the township of Ira, there is
an abandoned marble quarry adjacent to Bob Chapman's

farm. The Clarendon, a primary source of Otter Creek,
which in turn is a major tributary of Lake Champlain,
has a wide fertile flood plain. With only occasional me-
anders, the Clarendon is paralleled by an old right-of-way
grading leading to the quarry. At its northern end the
spur connected to the still operating Rutland Railroad.
The other end of the spur terminates at what was once
a linear marble mill, now in ruins.

Most of New England is dotted with cellars in varying
stages of feral decay. These pocks made of fieldstone, or
the later ones of concrete, very quickly disappear, not so
much like Central American ruins beneath dense underbrush, but through decomposition aided by the frost. The
foundation of the marble mill is a hodgepodge of rectangular blocks of white marble varying from a pound or
two to several tons. Abandoned since before W. W.
II, these slabs of scrap marble were so closely set that
even though no mortar was used in fitting them together,
there are no plants growing between the ashlar blocks.
The mill ruins are about a quarter of a mile long. At the
southerly end, on the verge of the quarry pit itself, can
be found the remains of the concrete anchors and iron
pivots of the booms. Quarry booms to this day are not
built of triangulated steel trusses like construction der-
ricks, but use virgin-growth Douglas firs from the Pacific
Northwest. These whole tree trunks were brought East
as deck cargo on clipper ships, whose masts were also
erected of Douglas fir. It seems particularly fitting that
the clippers, which were primarily built to carry passengers (they were not efficient bulk-cargo handlers) to
three successive gold rushes should be used to bring as

return cargo not only gold but irreplaceable timber to be used for Eastern quarrying. There is no more virgin wood, but at Barre, in eastern Vermont, where granite is quarried, they have a stock of nineteenth-century Douglas fir trunks which is expected to last at least another hundred years.

Beyond the boom mounts is the hole itself, approximately thirty by two hundred yards. Although there is no surface-water source and no visible runoff, there is no algae and the water is the color of an old Pennsylvania whiskey bottle and always colder than you expect or remember. Nobody knows how deep it is and its depth is a source of never-ending saloon speculation. The depth of a local hole always fascinates. Where I grew up, Lake Success was called bottomless, being a natural rather than man-made hole, and it was speculated that its pure cold water might come from Connecticut in an underground stream beneath Long Island Sound. Highly improbable considering that the Sound was formed by the halt of the last glacier and Long Island itself is the debris scraped along on its leading edge. To the best of my knowledge, as with Lake Success, nobody has ever made a serious attempt at fathoming the hole. The marble company's offices are six miles away in Proctor, and surely they have records, but that is hardly the way to go about such an inquiry.

Walking around the perimeter of the quarry or studying the U. S. Coast and Geodetic Survey aerial photographs of the West Rutland quadrant, the most profound feature of the landscape goes unnoticed. Near Easton, Pennsylvania, there are numerous similar abandoned

quarry holes, but surrounding them are waste piles rival-
ing John Huston's Welsh valley for achieved ugliness. In
Ira there is no visible waste. This is not through any
planned management or even through a later beautifica-
tion program, either of which might have been possible.
When I lived near Easton, it was the best joke they ever
heard in the local tavern when I suggested that the slate
company could dump its low-grade slate and shale back
into its empty pits rather than create ever larger eyesores.
The worst eyesores in Vermont are the rusted-out, abandoned cars which abound, but Vermont is the only state
to my knowledge which has a portable baling machine
which they send around the state collecting and demolish-
ing old cars. The baled scrap iron is then sold at a profit.

The scrap marble is there, in point of fact it starts no
more than twenty feet from the westerly edge of the hole
and extends over some thirty acres. That is an area twice
the size of the eventual site of the World Trade Center.
There is an adjacent meadow, also owned by the marble
company, of an additional fifteen acres that could have
absorbed half again as much waste if the hole had not
petered out.

The first indication that the waste is there when walking west from the hole's edge or when walking east from
Chapman's upper meadow is the cables. Laced through
the woods are woven-steel cables some an inch and a half
in diameter, the kind used on steam shovels and cranes.
I often cruise the woods on the high ground south of
Chapman's new house. Chapmans have been farming this
area for over a hundred years; on the marble lintel of the

house where Bob's mother now lives is carved "Geo. Chapman 1846." I was tracking a locally mythic ten-point whitetail buck that lives on Chapman's land (most Eastern deer go through their entire life cycle within an area of less than two square miles). After eight years of drought this has been a flush summer in central Vermont, so that tracks are easily followed in the soft ground. Chapman's land slopes off to the north down to the Ira and Clarendon, two of the best trout streams around, and this year there are well over forty revived rills and springs running either northeast or northwest through his woodlot. There were a great many tracks, but I was only concerned with where that particular whitetail watered and at what hours. Since the Ira runs in a gorge some forty feet deep in places, the deer tend towards the Clarendon, which is more accessible and where they have better brush cover.

Having seen all I could for one day, I headed due east from the high ground in the direction of the quarry and the road. Most of this area was heavily logged out for hardwoods in the 1880s and again for softwoods some thirty years later, but occasionally a live maple or hickory can be found, usually on high ground, with a trunk base of two feet or more that was left uncut because of lightning damage. I started noticing cables anchored to the few hardwood trees remaining in what is now mostly second- and third-growth hemlock, poplar, cedar and white pine, and running downhill towards the quarry. The pattern of the cables, or at least those that are not so buried as to be untraceable, is of huge omegas, the serifs of which are anchored to the trees in the woods, and the loops extending out and girdling man-made hills of drilled, blasted and sawn chunks of white marble.

All mining operations create waste heaps, and all slag and waste piles roughly take the form of a cone, unless they abut against a natural topography of greater magnitude. At Danby, about twenty five miles south of Ira, there is still in operation a most interesting quarry. Rather than an open pit, this quarry from the exterior appears to be a cave mouth in the side of heavily wooded Dorset Peak (3,804 feet). The mountain is visible from U. S. Route 7, the main north-south road through central Vermont, rising rapidly from the Otter Creek floodplain, which at that point is cradled between Emerald State Park and Green Mountain National Forest. Directly below the cave mouth is what appears to be a beautifully glinting white alluvial fan extending down to the plain.

Marble consists primarily of crystalline limestone of organic origin forged into a monolithic mass devoid of shear planes. The coloration of true marble (there are small quantities of stalagmitic and serpentine limestones sometimes called marble) is due to trace impurities, some of fossil origin but mostly metallic salts such as iron pyrites. Marble's most attractive property as an architectural and decorative material is that it can be polished. The etymology of our word "marble" traces back to the Greek μάρμᾰρος (pronounced "mármaros") meaning "shining stone." If not subjected to sulphureous attack, as by industrial city air or standing water, both of which blacken and then crumble its surface, polished marble will remain glittering. Rough-sawn marble has a dull surface much like that of other limestones, but fractured marble reveals thousands of rhombohedral cleavage planes that interlock to give this form of dolomite its uniform texture. In polished marble, particularly white statuary marble free of colored trace impurities, light penetrates beneath the smooth surface and is reflected back to the beholder, glinting off the crystal facets. This phenomenon of light penetration is also readily noticeable in well-used solid-brass doorknobs and belt buckles where light reflects the outlines of subsurface crystalline structure. Without speculating as to the state of Greek knowledge of molecular structure, it is worth noting that their term for gleaming metals such as polished bronze was μαρμάρεος (marmáreos).

The Dorset Peak fan is marble waste from the quarry, possibly better called a "mine." Once inside the entrance, it is unlike other quarries. There is a horizontal floor interrupted only by massive hewn columns of marble which support the vaulted ceiling. Slowly man is removing the pre-Cambrian compressed sedimentary layer of shellfish remains, leaving the upper third of a mountain peak supported on integral columns. Because diastrophic action is necessary for the great heat and pressure that form crystalline marble, it is very rare to find a sedimentary layer again horizontal and even rarer to find it raised well above the level of the surrounding countryside. In all, the Danby quarry may be the least offensive in appearance of all currently productive mining operations.

The Ira quarry, at the meeting of the Clarendon floodplain and the foot of the north slope of Susie Peak (2,409

feet) , is more conventionally located. It is likely that
more by expedience than aesthetics the waste piles were
started on the westerly side of the quarry so as not to
block the only practical transportation route. The waste
was moved up the slope to the west by chain buckets and
drag lines. Originally it was at least one hundred yards
from the pit edge to the foot of the steep slope up to
Chapman's upper meadow. It is no longer possible to
determine, and even the family cannot remember. As the
space beneath the drag line, which was anchored in the
woods above, filled up, the cables would be abandoned
and a new location set up about one hundred feet away.
Slowly a microcosm of a mountain range appeared. When
all the immediately available land was covered, a second
generation of waste piles was started on top of the first
by anchoring new, longer cables of even greater diameter
further up the slope.

The waste that went onto these piles varied from
pieces five feet square weighing many tons down through
marble dust. To this day the older operating marble mills
still use long, straight reciprocating saws clamped at both
ends, in appearance much like the woodsman's two-man
saw. These saw blades were flooded as they cut up the
quarried blocks. This water from the Clarendon served
both to cool the saw blades and to carry off the marble
dust from the fresh cut so as not to clog the teeth. At that
time the Clarendon was badly polluted with dust, which
made the water run milky and killed the trout. As much
of the wet dust as was deemed practical went up on the
waste dump in chain buckets.

Over the years rainwater has leached much of this dust

back down through the broken and cut marble, making what is again a monolithic mountain, needing only further succeeding sedimentary layers, pressure and heat to fuse it.

Approached from the east as you climb up the steep faces, the ground gradually changes from soil, to rock-studded soil, to rock-studded white dust, eventually to piled rock. But unlike any rock outcropping to be found in nature, it is all sharp edges or generated flat planes.

Approached from the west, the transition is much less gradual. Walking down a slight incline in the woods, the land suddenly changes direction, going sharply up for twenty or thirty feet, and you emerge on a barren white peak leeched free of any soil. Within twenty feet of the other side of the peak poplars have taken root, lower down there are stands of white pine, and at the base hundreds of feet down are thick blackberry brambles. Beneath the surface, more noticeable when climbing up than from the top, are the lairs of rattlesnake, woodchuck, fox and porcupine burrowed into the dust between the broken rock fragments. They must leave the rock pile every day as there is no water available except the run-off immediately following a storm and during the spring thaw. On the rock pile they move freely and seem less fearful in the presence of a quiet man than the same species a few hundred yards away in the woods.

Given time, soil will accrete by wind and plant decomposition and the chemical breakdown of the limestone. Given time, wind and water and frost will wear down the peaks and fill in the lower crags. Given time, water from the woods will start to flow down the surfaces of the cairn. One windfall is enough to divert a spring. By the time the tree trunk rots out completely, about ten years for softwoods, a natural earthen dam will have been deposited which will be strong enough to hold the water on its new course. Once there is a steady water supply, the larger mammals, deer, catamounts and bear, will return. The abundance of large rocks forms good shelter and places for hibernation.

Stephen Dedalus uses the metaphor of a bird and a mountain of sand to indicate the vastness of his conception of eternity. It should not be taken as impertinent to say that on the day that I inadvertently found those rip-rap peaks, on the uppermost stone was the beginnings of organic soil—a pile of bird shit.